Marjorie Macnaught
Section A.

THE TALE THAT HAD
NO ENDING

BOOKS FOR THE STORY-TELLER

STORIES TO TELL AND HOW TO
TELL THEM

By ELIZABETH CLARK

Illustrated by GLADYS M. REES

MORE STORIES AND HOW TO
TELL THEM

By ELIZABETH CLARK

Illustrated by NINA K. BRISLEY

THE BOOK OF THE CAT
JEREMIAH

By FRANCESCA CLAREMONT

Illustrated by GLADYS M. REES

3/6 *net per volume*

UNIVERSITY OF LONDON PRESS, LTD.
10 & 11 WARWICK LANE, LONDON, E.C.4

THE TALE THAT HAD NO ENDING

AND OTHER STORIES

BY ELIZABETH CLARK

ILLUSTRATED BY NINA K. BRISLEY

UNIVERSITY OF LONDON PRESS LTD.

10 & 11 WARWICK LANE, LONDON, E.C.4

1929

First Printed September 1929

Printed in Great Britain for the UNIVERSITY OF LONDON PRESS, LTD.,
by HAZELL, WATSON AND VINEY, LTD., London and Aylesbury.

TO ALL THE FRIENDS, KNOWN AND UNKNOWN

OF THE PRESENT OR OF THE PAST,

WHO HAVE HELPED ME TO FIND

STORIES AND TO TELL THEM

I GRATEFULLY DEDICATE

THIS BOOK

CONTENTS

INTRODUCTION
A STORY-TELLER'S NOTE-BOOK

MOST of the stories in this book—to be exact, eleven of them—have already been published, with their accompanying comments, in *Child Education*. The remaining two, " Yogodagu and the Bees of Yamato " and " The Tale that Had no Ending," appear in print—in their present form that is—for the first time. " Yogodagu and the Bees of Yamato" is adapted, by permission of Messrs. A. and C. Black, from " How Yogodagu Won a Battle," contained in *Ancient Tales and Folk-lore of Japan* by Richard Gordon Smith. I have also to express my sincere thanks to Mr. Arthur Mee for his kindness in connection with the use I have made of his version of " The Tale that Had no Ending."

As in the case of previous books, I have drawn on legend or folk-lore (and in one instance on a personal reminiscence) for the source or suggestion of all the stories in this volume. I have given the origin of each tale in the comments partly by way of acknowledgment of my debts, but also because I think it may be useful to some other story-teller to know the seed, so to speak, from which a story has grown. There are not nearly enough " ready-made " stories for telling ; and experience teaches that, to supply our need, we story-tellers must keep our eyes wide open for every opportunity of storing up material out of which good stories may be made.

Mr. Arthur Burrell has dealt at length with this subject in his invaluable book *A Guide to Story-tellers*.[1] There, as many of us know, are to be found, beside much else, stories, germs of stories, sources of material, and suggestions for dealing with it and classifying it when found. I can add nothing to all that Mr. Burrell has given us out of his wide knowledge and long experience of the lore of story-telling. But I can here express my gratitude for his advice—given long ago, when I first tried my hand at story-telling—that I should keep a Story-teller's Note-book. That advice I have followed, not as methodically as I should, I own, but enthusiastically and with perseverance. As a result I possess a series of Note-books, containing a queer medley of useful material. There are names and notes of stories from books that I could not afford to buy (with,

[1] *A Guide to Story-tellers.* By Arthur Burrell. Pitman.

of course, the title, author and publisher of each book) ; one should never lose track of a good story. There are scraps of folk- and fairy-lore, tales of flowers and beasts and birds, or little legends of saints. Many of these are very shortly and poorly told ; they have come from such sources as guide-books (relics of holidays, near or far afield), books on county history or folk-lore, on travel or natural history. There are also notes and quotations that may help with the settings of stories, because " seeing is believing " where a story is concerned. To be able to visualise a scene clearly is a great help towards telling the tale with conviction and assurance.

One learns never to disregard anything that seems as if it might have the makings of a story. No matter how brief and bald a scrap it may be, down it goes in the note-book. There is always the hope that one may find information by means of which it may be amplified, or another version to supplement it. Besides, sometimes a story has a way of growing into something by itself— especially if one knows or has read about the place which gave it birth. It may remain a dry little husk for years, and then one day, as one looks at it, it begins to take colour and expand like those queer little Japanese flowers made of pith, which bloom so magically when dropped into a glass of water. And sometimes those brief and tantalising notes of stories to be found in such books as Grimms' *Teutonic Mythology* and other records of folk-lore suddenly seem like the end of a string—a " tag." We begin to consider, and lo ! there is a tale unwinding itself. In fact, like the godmother in Mrs. Ewing's story [1] who " did not trust herself to design a figure," one may not trust oneself to make a story, but—imitating her observation and ingenious industry—one can sometimes " grow," as gardeners say, a story from a cutting or a seed. This is a paragraph of fearfully mixed metaphors, but they all seem necessary to explain the ways of embryo stories, so I will not try to correct them.

But I must not forget one other item that my Story-teller's Note-book contains, and that is a collection of newspaper-cuttings. It is a good plan to be on the watch (and to ask our friends to be also) for the short paragraphs containing stories of birds, animals—clever things done by them, kindly acts done to them—which are now and again to be found in the daily press. We often pass them by ; yet they contain excellent

[1] *Old Father Christmas.* By J. H. Ewing.

material for the true stories of familiar creatures that we need especially for little children.

Here, for instance, is a cutting from the *Daily Mail*—undated, I am sorry to say. One should always mark cuttings with date and source. It is often useful to know to what season of the year a story belongs ; so many details depend upon it. Also we may possibly need to ask for further information.

" Living in the village of B., in Yorkshire, there is a cat which has saved the lives of three people.

" Yesterday morning Mr. P. got up as usual soon after 4 a.m., lighted the kitchen fire, and left the house to go to work soon after 5, leaving his wife, his son, and his daughter, still asleep.

" About 6.30 a.m. the girl was awakened by Nippy, the cat, jumping on her bed and patting her face. Directly he saw that she was awake, the cat rushed to Mrs. P.'s room and woke her also. At the time the rooms were full of suffocating smoke.

" Mrs. P. called to her son, and the three, putting wet towels round their faces, fought their way downstairs through dense clouds of smoke which came from the kitchen, where the mantelpiece and fittings were well alight. When they reached the yard the cat, which had come with them, collapsed, and for some time it seemed doubtful if it would recover. Meanwhile neighbours had come to the rescue and had put out the fire.

" ' If it had not been for Nippy, I am quite sure we should all have been suffocated,' said Mrs. P. to a *Daily Mail* representative."

Little more than an introduction to " Nippy " is needed in order to make of this quite a useful ten-minutes story. " This is going to be a true story about a cat named Nippy " we may begin. It is permissible I think to describe Nippy's colour and size—scrupulous story-tellers can preface this by " I think he was . . ." We tell where he lived, of the family and of Nippy's standing in the household. (He must have been a friend of the family I think, otherwise he would have been simply " the cat ".) We tell how Nippy slept in the kitchen and kept the house clear of mice, and then begins the story. "Well—one cold winter's morning . . ." (It must have been a cold or windy morning, possibly both.) We picture Nippy's uneasiness—the rush up the stairs to the sleeping family, the little patting paws and anxious mewings, the rescue and Nippy's happy recovery—a true " they-lived-happily-ever-after " ending.

Here is another cutting from the *Daily Telegraph* of July 1928.

" Traffic in the City was held up for about a quarter of an hour yesterday while a newly-fledged pigeon, which had fallen into the street, was restored to its parents.

" The youngster, apparently taking its first flight, managed to escape from the street on to a ledge a few feet from the ground, but despite encouragement from its agitated parents was unable to get any farther. Relief came in the shape of a policeman, who sent for a ladder, and a kindly passer-by, who mounted to the neighbourhood of the second floor and replaced the young pigeon in its nest."

This seems less promising. But when working it out with students, I found it had more possibilities than at first appear. We began by imagining a pigeon's nest, high up on some ledge or cornice of a tall London building, with the roaring street below. We saw the two baby pigeons hatched and we listened to the admonitions of Father and Mother Pigeon as we watched the little ones learning to fly. We named them—not very originally—" Coo " and " Coo-coo." Names are a great help in handling a story ; the characters become more real and much confusion of pronouns and personalities is avoided. Then one day we saw Coo full-fledged, but still unpractised, lose his balance and flutter helplessly to the street, while Mother Pigeon called in vain. We watched the big policeman stand over the frightened bird with upraised arm, the city-traffic piling up behind him—lorries, vans, buses, taxis, carts—all waiting till Coo was picked up, and finally we saw the ladder brought and the bird put safely back in the nest.

And here is yet another cutting from the *Christian Science Monitor*, of March 1928, taken from the Sundial Column, with its motto " I Record only the Sunny Hours," in which daily, two or three stories of kindly acts are published.

" A woman who very often enjoys a walk through Kensington Gardens noticed one day a very plump little sparrow hop slowly over the grass to a large tree. After the sparrow went a tall uniformed official of the gardens.

" When the tree was reached an amusing

game of hide-and-seek began. Round and round the tree hopped the sparrow, and round and round after it went the big man. But man's wit, opposed to bird's wit, soon won the contest. The man reversed his steps, and coming face to face with the sparrow, stooped down to pick it up.

" Whereupon the sparrow, not at all hurried or alarmed, fluttered heavily up to a limb, where it settled itself comfortably.

" ' You and that bird seem to know each other very well,' said the interested spectator. Then the mystery was explained.

" ' That sparrow's eaten too much, and it's so full it can't fly,' said the official. ' When I see them like that I go and pick them up, and throw them up into a tree.' And smiling over the incident the kindly giant strode away to a point of vantage.

" The woman smiled, too, as she thought how often she came across such gentle actions in the big city."

I have often used this story and it always gives delight. It is so pleasantly put before us that it is easy to tell it at rather greater length. And Kensington Gardens is so familiar to most children, Londoners or not, through their beloved Peter Pan, that they will probably have some idea of the setting of the story. I always like to think of it as happening somewhere near the Round Pond and the Broad Walk, where children and buns, and consequently sparrows, most do congregate. It sounds, too, as if the keeper and the sparrow and the lady had the Gardens almost to themselves, so probably it was on some cold bright evening of very early spring when the children had gone home to tea and the officials were going their rounds before closing-time.

I must only mention one more newspaper-story, and that by way of a sad example of a neglected opportunity. In the Casual Column of the *Glasgow Herald* of March 5th, 1928, allusion is made to " a London firm " which " created a precedent a few days ago by pensioning off the office cat, which is now to receive half-a-crown a week for life. On the occasion of its retiral pussy was presented with a velvet collar with its name in silver letters." What a worthy companion is here for Dick Whittington's famous cat, or for Puss in Boots himself! But alas! I did not follow up the story by making enquiries as to that pussy's honourable and hard-working career or as to its abodes, past and present—

and so a good tale was lost. Let story-tellers take warning !

So much for newspaper cuttings. I have talked more perhaps than was necessary about them and their possibilities, but I am anxious to make clear how much good material for stories is missed by neglecting them. Now for a few words about another type of story—that which can be evolved out of some scrap of folk-lore, legend or short fable.

Take for instance Æsop's fable of " The Frog Who Wished to be as Big as an Ox."

" An Ox, grazing in a meadow, chanced to set his foot on a young Frog and crushed him to death. His brothers and sisters who were playing near, at once ran to tell their Mother what had happened. ' The monster that did it, Mother, was such a size,' said they. The Mother who was a vain old thing thought that she could easily make herself as large. ' Was it as big as this?' she asked, blowing and puffing herself out. ' Oh, much bigger than that,' replied the young Frogs. ' As this then,' cried she, puffing and blowing again with her might. ' Nay, Mother,' said they, ' if you were to try till you burst yourself you would never be so big.' The silly old Frog tried to puff herself out still more and burst herself indeed."

Now if we are going to adapt material—whether it be for the making of a frock or a story—our first step must be consideration of its extent and possibilities. Here, therefore, we see that we have : an Ox in a meadow—a young Frog crushed by his hoof—brother and sister Frogs who rush to tell their Mother, a foolish ignorant and vain creature who tries to put herself on an equality with the Ox, and bursts in the attempt.

We promptly cut out the incident of the crushed frog. All that is necessary to the story is the report of the immensity of the ox and crushed frogs are a sad and unpleasant spectacle.

Further—Æsop may have thought that Frogs gathered their offspring around them like chickens, but most children know far too much about the free and independent tadpole to suppose that frogs cultivate family feelings. So *Mother* frog had better go. What have we left ? Quite a funny little story of a small frog, tremendously impressed by an enormous creature which it had never seen before, rushing to tell a large frog who, vain and ignorant, puffs himself up in emulation till he bursts.

Now what about the bursting? A bursting frog is all very well in a fable, the ending of which is designedly short and sharp ; it is the moral, not the story which is intended to affect us. But a story—especially a story for children —is a different matter. It is largely a series of pictures and we are meant to see and consider it, to dwell upon it in detail. And a bursting frog is not a probable, and certainly not a pretty, spectacle. I thought I had successfully countered this difficulty when I remembered that frogs, like other reptiles, change their skins. It seemed that a frog might burst his skin and yet survive, with only loss of dignity. But I discovered that frogs only shed a thin membrane ; toads on the other hand shuffle off the whole skin. Something spectacular was certainly needed, and so my frog had to become " Mr. T. Toad " of page 159 in this book.

Now for another problem. It is well, when first thinking out a story, to look out for all pit-falls and snags. If we come upon them when we are well under way they may completely upset our story. They should be seen and provided against beforehand. The point now in question is : how was it that the frog—or Mr. T. Toad—had never seen an ox ? Apparently the creature had no idea of anything bigger than itself; puffed up with ignorance and pride it really thought it could not be surpassed. We must, therefore, make it clear that our Mr. T. Toad had a very limited horizon and was completely cut off from the world. That is why the story, as I have told it, begins by telling of the little pool hidden away among the bulrushes and brambles. The business of the introduction is to clear the way for the story.

It is well, I think, when putting a story in shape for telling, to remember the structure of the Folk-tale. The Folk-tale lived and was handed down by being told and re-told to one generation after another, and it shaped itself accordingly. "Once upon a time"—or in some such fashion—it begins. It tells us just what it is needful to know—of the Queen who wished for a daughter "as white as snow, as red as blood, and as black as ebony"; of the "very rich gentleman and he'd three daughters, and he thought he'd see how fond they were of him"; of the "poor widow who had an only son named Jack and a cow that was all her fortune." And then straightway follows the story. In fact the Folk-tale begins at the beginning and goes on to the end, and that, I believe, is usually the best plan for us story-tellers to follow. It is all very well for *writers* of stories to begin in the middle with an arresting ejaculation or situation. The reader is quite content to be first startled, thrilled, puzzled or intrigued and then to be led back to the beginning and on again to the end. The printed word is there to be a record, a reference, an assurance ; one can go fast or slow, read and re-read at will. But story-teller and listener must be together ; if the listener is bewildered, he is lost.

So—in this tale—after explaining where Mr. T. Toad lived. I have gone on to tell his story, and I have done my best to let it be clearly seen that he was a Toad who fairly asked for trouble. In the fable we are told that the puffed-up mother-frog was a " vain and ignorant creature." That is enough for us older folk ; we know only too well what ignorance and vanity mean and how unpleasantly they can make us behave. But the child does not know, and it is of no use to merely enumerate the qualities of Mr. T. Toad. We must tell about him, make him reveal himself in his words and works and ways.

Here, I know, is the point at which some readers will say despairingly, " But we have no imagination ; we can't *make up* Mr. T. Toad's

words and works and ways." I do not think it is
"imagination" that is needed so much as
common sense and industry. We have the
main lines of the plot and the personality of the
chief character to guide us. We have thought
out our introduction and have provided the Toad
with a dwelling-place. Then let us reflect :
what kind of a neighbour would he be ? how
would he treat his friends ? who would be the
inhabitants of the little pool ? Picture him and
his surroundings, watch him, consider the cir-
cumstances and soon we shall begin to see that
he is speaking and acting for himself. Then
I believe the wise proceeding is to scribble down
what we see. Nothing clears one's thoughts so
well. Diffidence, perplexity, *laziness* will try to
hold us up at this point. But do not let them ;
the great thing is to begin—somehow, anyhow—
and once begun the story goes on. And if it
sticks at any point, we stop and look and presently
scribble again.

So the tale unrolls until we come to the ending.
And the ending of a story, like the beginning,
needs care and thought in the telling. It must
be satisfactory and it must be complete. " Satisfactory," of course, may mean tragic, comic,
comfortable, consoling or sentimental according

to the trend of the story. But whatever it may be, we must tell it so that our listeners may feel we have reached the only possible conclusion of the matter. And it must be complete ; we must neither stint nor waste words, but the tale must be well and truly finished, there must be no ragged ends. The Folk-tale—once again—is a good model. It attends to matters thoroughly, if at times a little drastically. " So Snow-white and the Prince were married and they lived happily ever after. But the wicked Queen was put into a barrel full of sharp nails and they rolled her down the hill." (I am not recommending this as a desirable ending, but it is certainly complete !)

And so, when telling of the fate of Mr. T. Toad, it seemed also necessary to glance at the ensuing peace and prosperity of his friends and neighbours.

Here then, ends the tale. It is a very small tale and I seem to have spent a disproportionate amount of time and space in discussing it. I hope I have not made the building-up of the story sound too laborious an affair. It is not really so. Putting stories together for telling is really a delightful game, if only it be played with good-will, intelligence, and a spice of humour. " You never know *what* you can do till you try," says the proverb ; which is only another way of reminding us that many folk—nobody knows how many— never attain because they never attempt. And that is just as true of this game of story-making as it is of everything else in life.

THE TALE THAT HAD NO ENDING

I

THIS is a very old story. It is so old that I think Daniel may have heard some of it at the Court of the Kings of Babylon. Solomon may have known one like it, and Moses may have listened to such a tale in the Palace of Pharaoh. In one way or another it has been told for hundreds of years. It is the Story of the King and the Tale that had no ending.

Now there was once a King who loved Stories. He loved them so much that he would have them told to him at all hours of the day, and at any hour of the night. He went to sleep listening to one Story and as soon as he awoke he asked for another. He listened to Stories when he was eating and when he ought to have been governing his Kingdom. And there were not enough Stories to satisfy that King. All the Stories in the Kingdom were told and told again. The King's Soldiers went out and conquered distant lands, and with their spoil and their prisoners they brought back Stories for the King. The King's Merchants sailed to far countries, and with their merchandise they brought back Stories for the King. And the King's Wise Men dived deep into books written in old, forgotten tongues and found there more Stories for the King. And still there were not enough Stories. And as the Stories became fewer the King's temper grew worse. One Story-teller after another came to the end of his Stories and, as each poor man could tell no more, the King said : " Away with him ! " and the Story-teller was hurried off to prison.

And, as the supply of Story-tellers and Stories grew less and less, the people of that land grew most anxious and unhappy, for they said, " What will he do when there are *none* ! " Nobody liked to think of that dreadful day, or of how angry the King would be.

But just as things began to look very black

indeed, the King had a bright idea. He thought
how splendid it would be if he could find a
man who could tell him a Story that would go
on for ever. All the Stories that had been told
to him had come to an end and had left him
wanting more.
But a Story that
never ended, that
would go on from
day to day, all
day and all night
if he desired,
would make him
perfectly happy.
" And if I found
such a man,"
thought the King,
" he should marry
my daughter and
rule half the

Kingdom. Then I should have a son-in-law
always at hand to tell me a Story and I should
be perfectly content."

So Proclamation was made all the world
over—East and West and North and South—
that the man who could tell the King a Story-
without-end, should marry the Princess and

take half the Kingdom. From all the four quarters of the world Story-tellers came flocking, for the Kingdom was large and rich and the Princess was said to be exceedingly beautiful. And no one paid much attention to the end of the Proclamation which said : " But any man whose Story does not last for ever shall have his head cut off." For they all felt quite certain that their Stories would succeed. But when they came to the Palace and heard how many Story-tellers had told Stories to the King and how they were all in prison, because they knew no more, one and all went away again, for nobody wanted to have his head cut off.

So the Princess remained unmarried, and there was no one at all to tell Stories to the King.

But one day there came to the Palace a man who said that he was quite sure he could tell the King a Story that never would end.

" I will tell it upon one condition," he said. " I must be allowed to tell it in my own way and nobody must stop me."

And the King, who was very glad to hear that he was to have a Story at last, said graciously, " Certainly. I give my royal word that he shall tell the Story as he pleases, and I will listen as long as it lasts."

So the King put on his royal robes and sat upon his throne. The Courtiers gathered round him. And when the Story-teller had bowed low before the King, he stood up and began his Story.

"O King!" he said. "There was once a King, a great King, a rich King, a splendid

King, even such a King as thou, O King! And this King built a great Granary. He built it of stone and he roofed it with stone. And when it was built he placed in it all the corn that was reaped that year in his Kingdom, so that the Granary was filled even to the very roof. Then that King walled up the windows and barred the doors; and he said to himself, 'Now, I have a great store of corn against a

31

time of famine.' *But*, O King!" said the
Story-teller, "that King did not know that there
was a little chink between the stones of the walls
where the builders had not pressed down the
mortar. And there came, O King! a great
army of ants, many millions of ants, so that the
earth was black with them. And an ant went
in at the little chink and came out with a grain
of corn ; and another ant went in at the little
chink and came out with a grain of corn ; and
another ant went in at the little chink and came
out with a grain of corn ; and another ant went
in at the little chink and came out with a grain
of corn ; and another ant went in at the little
chink and came out with a grain of corn ;
and another ant went in at the little chink." . . .
"*Stop!*" shouted the King. "Tell me no
more of grains of corn ! Tell me what happened
to that King ! "

But the Story-teller looked at the King and
he shook his head. "O King ! " said he.
"Remember the promise is that I may tell
this story in my own way, and so am I telling it.
How can I tell the end before I have told the
beginning ? There are yet many millions of
ants and many millions of grains of corn."

The King was greatly ashamed to think that

32

he had forgotten his promise. He could not say another word. And, taking no more notice of him, the Story-teller continued : " And another ant went in at the little chink and came out with a grain of corn ; and another ant went in at the little chink and came out with a grain of corn ; and another ant went in at the little chink and came out with a grain of corn. . . ." He went on all that evening without stopping for an instant, till the King was so sleepy that they all went to bed.

And everyone dreamed of ants and grains of corn !

The next morning came and the Story-teller was ready to go on with his Story. The King put on his royal robe and sat upon his throne. The Courtiers gathered round him and every-one hoped that the ants were soon coming to an end. And the Story-teller began : " And another ant went in at the little chink and came out with a grain of corn." He went on all that day ; he went on all that week ; he went on all that month. Nobody dared stop him to ask when the ants were coming to an end. Everyone was tired—more tired than can be told—of hearing about ants, but the Story-teller never seemed weary of telling. He was always ready to brightly begin : " And *another* ant went in at the little chink and came out with a grain of corn."

The King began to look for excuses for not listening to the Story. He turned his mind to governing his Kingdom. He held long conversations with his Ministers. He made good laws and listened to the troubles and complaints of his subjects. He was a much better King than he had ever been before, but he was not happy. He had wanted a Story-without-end and it seemed as if he had certainly got one, and now that he had found it he did not like it at all. But he had given his Royal word to listen while the Story lasted and whenever he had a spare moment the Story-teller was always waiting to tell him of more and more ants and grains of corn.

At last he could bear it no longer ; and one day when the Story-teller began : " And another ant. . . ."

" Oh, man ! " said the poor King. " Is there no end to these ants ? "

And the Story-teller replied, " There is no end in sight, O King ! for there are yet innumerable ants and unnumbered grains of corn."

" Then tell me no more," shouted the King. " It is indeed a Story-without-end. Therefore, marry the Princess ; take half the Kingdom ; but tell me no more of these abominable ants ! "

And the Story-teller bowed. I think there was a twinkle in his eye. Perhaps he had been waiting for the King to say just that all the time, and was only surprised that he had waited so long. He stopped his Story ; he took half the Kingdom ; he married the Princess. The King set all the other poor Story-tellers free from prison and they came back one by one to Court and told their Stories, and the King found he was quite glad to listen. It was such a pleasant change after hearing of so many ants ! His new son-in-law helped him to govern and was a wise ruler and a good husband.

So everyone was happy—the King, the King's son-in-law, the Princess and the people of that

Kingdom. And the story ends as all stories should, " They lived happily ever after."

COMMENTS ON THE STORY

This is, in essentials, a very old story. There are many ways of telling it. In an Indian version a Fox outwits the tyrant King-Lion (who demands " stories without ceasing ") with a tale of fish escaping from a hole in a net. " First one fish escaped ; then two fish escaped ; then three fish. . . ." " Had I not been bound by my word to listen," says the angry Lion, " it had gone hard with thee." There is a Persian tale of an old Shepherd who tells the King of a countless flock of goats. There are other versions dealing with multitudes of ants or of locusts. In one variant the story has become a nursery tale (calculated to put any small person to sleep) of an unending flock of sheep passing over a bridge. And there are probably many others. The story, as I have told it here, is founded on a version which appeared in Vol. I of Harmsworth's *Children's Encyclopædia*.

I have told it many times. It is an excellent story to tell, but it has proved very hard to write down. It depends—more, I think, than any tale I know—upon the story-teller. There is so little actual plot, and what there is, is so thinly probable, that unless the story-teller puts really good work into the telling the story will not " go down."

It should begin—after the prelude as to its antiquity—with a certain amount of pomp and circumstance. The King, we feel, was an Eastern Potentate and his introduction to the audience demands a rather deliberate weightiness of speech—a good many capital letters, as it were. " There was Once a King Who Loved Stories. . . . And there were Not Enough Stories to Satisfy that King. . . . The King's Soldiers went out and conquered Distant Lands and with their Spoil and their Captives they brought back Stories for the King. The King's Merchants. . . ." So we continue until the tale of the unfortunate story-tellers is told.

Then we turn from the King to the contemplation of his dilemma and the tone becomes more confidential and conversational—more chatty, in fact! He was a Great King—but he was in a terrible fix none the less—what is he to do about it? Then comes his bright idea—the proclamation—the crowd of competition—their departure when they realise the danger of the adventure and, finally, the advent of the confident story-teller. All this is to be told, I think, much as one would relate an ordinary experience.

Then we get a glimpse of the Potentate again. " The King put on His Royal Robes and Sat upon His Throne. . . ." And the story of the ants begins magnificently, also : " There was Once a King—a Great King—a Rich King— a Splendid King—Even Such a King as Thou, O King ! " It is all rather measured and imposing—the King—the Great Granary. " He Built it of Stone and He Roofed it with Stone " —even the " little Chink between the Stones "— and finally the " Great Army of Ants, the Earth was Black with Them."

And now comes the real crux of the story, the phrase on which all depends, " and an ant went in at the little chink and came out with a grain of corn." How are we to handle its many repetitions ? One thing is sure, we must not be uncertain or apologetic (" I-know-this-is-silly-and-no-one-would-believe-it-but-it's-part-of-the-story "). We must not be bored and we must not be careless. The words are ridiculous, but so was the King when he expected a story without end. And the Story-teller is a person of calm common-sense who is taking the King at his word and is giving him, literally, what he asked for. And remember, as he told, he undoubtedly saw those ants ; in his mind's eye he saw them, " many millions of ants." He saw the Great Granary with its enormous hewn stones, its walled-up windows and fast-sealed doors, its heaped-up treasure of wheat " even to the roof," and the tiny chink in those invulnerable walls where the little black ants go in and out. He saw it all, and so must we. Solemnly and calmly, as he did, we tell the tale of those ants. It is quite matter-of-fact ; there they are, coming and going, coming and going. We could tell of them for ever. It is rather—if I may be excused the simile—like reading an interminable laundry list.

How many repetitions are we to give ? That depends on ourselves and on our audience. I find it a good plan to go solemnly on *till the listeners laugh*—and then a little longer. About three times usually evokes preliminary squeaks ; after two more the joke has probably dawned on everybody, and perhaps one gives yet another two for good measure. By that time one is usually laughing too !

The King's protest is emphatic, but he is

quite put out of countenance by the reminder of his promise. And the argument of the Story-teller is so simple. "How can I tell the end before the beginning?" he says. He is a little aggrieved. All that is needed is just a little reasonableness—*surely* it must be plain. . . . And the ants continue.

Then we take up our narrative again and tell of the relentless Story-teller, of the poor King's weariness, and of his final outburst. It must be made quite clear that the King admits that the Story-teller has fulfilled the condition ; then we can come triumphantly to the winding up of events. Everything clears up and cheers up. We tell it just as we should give an experience of our own. "After all, I *hadn't* waited at the wrong entrance. She was only a little late. And we went out and had lunch and did a matinée. Everything was all right and we had a jolly afternoon." That is exactly the note of the category which ends with, " And they lived happily ever after."

As I look back over the pages I have written, I realise that the comments are almost as long as the story. And some reader may say, "What a deal of fuss over a small matter " ;

while another may add, " Can one Story-teller really advise another how to tell any story ? Is it not, after all, too individual, too personal an affair ? "

Yes, I think it is. But once in a way it may be helpful to meet a story worked out in detail. Those who read and disagree with the advice will thereby (I hope) be made all the more sure as to how *they* would tell the tale. For there are as many ways as there are tellers ; the great thing is to *have* a way. Those who are all at sea, may be helped over this story and will perhaps gain some glimmerings which may be useful in the preparation of other stories. And those who have never thought much about story-telling may perhaps be led to think that there is more " to it " than they have hitherto realised. At any rate that is my hope, especially as regards the last-named class of reader, and that is my excuse for writing at such length.

YOGODAGU and the BEES of YAMATO

II

A Swarm of Bees in May
Is worth a Load of Hay.
A Swarm of Bees in June
Is worth a Silver Spoon.
But a Swarm in July—
You had best let 'em fly!

THAT is an English rhyme about Bees and it
makes one think of comfortable things like sweet-
scented clover and hay-fields and honeycomb
and shining golden honey trickling out of a
silver spoon. But there is an old story about
Bees that is told in Japan, which has nothing
to do with such things as these. It tells of a
very great Swarm of Bees that was so powerful
that it put to flight an army. It is the story of
Yogodagu and the Bees of Yamato.

Long ago, almost a thousand years ago, lived

Yogodagu, a prince and a warrior of Japan. He built a strong castle in a wild and lonely part of the province of Yamato, and there he lived and ruled the country-side. But a powerful enemy came against him with an army, and in a battle Yogodagu and his followers were defeated. Yogodagu and twenty of his men escaped, and they fled away and came by night to a little valley deep among the mountains of Kasagi. There they hid themselves in a cave among the rocks and trees and rested, and bound up their wounds.

They were afraid that their enemies had followed them even there ; but a whole day passed and there was no sign or sound of armed men. Another day came and went safely and at sunrise on the third day, Yogodagu came boldly out of his hiding-place and stood looking up and down the valley. He was wounded ; he was hungry and weary. He had no home, his friends and followers were scattered far and wide, and his enemy was hunting him like a wild beast. And yet, as Yogodagu stood there, on that morning of early summer, he was not thinking of his sorrows and troubles and fears. He smiled to himself for joy. "Yamato is a very fair land," he said.

43

For the valley was most beautiful. It lay in shadow, for the sun had not yet climbed above the mountain-tops, but overhead the sky was blue and behind the eastern hills was golden light. The south wind rustled softly among the young green leaves and set the flowers  nodding in the grass. It was a lovely, peaceful place.

And as Yogo-d a g u watched, the sun climbed higher in the sky and looked down into the valley. It touched the tree tops and lit the mountain-side. The leaves of the Oaks were golden in the morning light, the young shoots of the Maples were tipped with crimson. The wild Wistaria hung in long trails of misty blue among the branches, the Bamboos shone like emeralds, and the Azaleas were like clouds at sunset, pink and amber and orange and rose.

Presently, as he stood there, Yogodagu noticed that a cluster of flowers on a bush near-by was

44

nodding and shaking as if it were being tossed by a little wind. He moved closer and stooped to look. Then he saw that a great Spider had spun his web from flower to flower and into the web had blundered a little brown Bee. It was struggling to escape, and in its struggles it shook the web and the rosy Azalea flowers, while the Spider sat watching and waiting to seize it when it should be too tired to sting.

"My honourable little friend," said Yogodagu to the Bee, "I, too, have an enemy who watches and waits to kill me and it seems that I may not be able to escape. But I can set you free to fly."

And he bent down and broke the web and carefully lifted the Bee with a twig and set it in the cup of a flower. Then he stood watching while it cleaned itself from the sticky, clinging strands of web, till it spread its wings and darted away like a little shining spark in the sunlight. And Yogodagu sighed and wished that he could come and go as freely and happily as the little brown Bee. All that day he thought and planned, but there seemed no way of escape for him and his faithful men.

Now that night as Yogodagu slept, he dreamed a dream. He thought that he stood in the valley and a man came to him, a little man in brown and gold with a sharp and shining dagger at his side.

"Honourable Sir," said the man, "I am the Bee whom you helped; and now in my turn I will help you. There are millions of Bees in Yamato and all will come at my call. This must you do. Build in this valley a house to shelter you and your men and round it build a wall that will shelter the Bees. And have no fear.

My people will fight for you in time of need and you shall escape your enemy."

Yogodagu awoke. The sun was climbing above the mountain tops, the wind was rustling among the trees. And he remembered how he had walked among the flowers and how he had let the little Bee go free. He thought of the dream that had come to him in the night, and he resolved to follow the Bee-man's advice.

So, at the end of the valley, he and his men built a little house to shelter them, and round it they made a wall of hollow logs and stones and stumps of trees, all loosely piled together to make a dwelling for the Bees. And when all was ready, the Bees came. From hollow rocks and trees, from caves and crevices in the mountain sides, from far and near they came in buzzing swarms, and they settled in the place that Yogodagu had made for them. More and more came, till all day long the air was filled with the sound of their humming wings. Even by night could be heard the soft and sleepy murmur of them—thousands and thousands of Bees, all guarding the house of Yogodagu.

Then, one day a messenger came running from a friendly village, with news for Yogodagu. His enemy had heard of the house in the valley; and he was on his way with a band of men to drive Yogodagu from that shelter as he had driven him from his castle and his lands.

The messenger begged Yogodagu to fly further into the mountains, but Yogodagu refused. He remembered the Bee-man's promise and he did not try to escape. So when his enemy with his army came to the valley they saw Yogodagu and his men standing before their house. They looked ready to fight ; their spears shone in the sunlight and their bows were drawn. But as the enemy drew near it seemed that Yogodagu's men were only cowards after all. They shot a few arrows and then turned and ran into the house.

The enemy's men shouted ; their leader laughed. " Charge," he said, " Break down their miserable wall. Kill Yogodagu and scatter his men like dead leaves in autumn." His men rushed forward ; up to the clumsy wall they came. They crashed into it. Down went the wall ; and up from its ruins, with a roar of wings, rose a great dark cloud of Bees. Thousands and thousands there were; the air was black with them.

In one moment the enemy's army turned and fled and behind them came the angry Bees of Yamato.

What happened to the leader I do not know ; I only know that his army was scattered far and wide, and never again did he trouble Yogodagu. And Yogodagu with his men went back to the castle from which they had been driven and he lived there happily for many years to come.

And he did not forget his faithful friends the Bees. For when the battle was over, he and his men gathered up the little brown bodies of those who had fallen in the fight. (The sad thing about Bees is that they nearly always die after they sting. They hurt themselves more than they hurt their enemy.) Then they buried them in one grave, and over it they built a Temple. And year by year when the month of May came round, Yogodagu journeyed to the little valley among the Mountains. And there he prayed and  made offerings and gave thanks in the Temple that he had built, in remembrance of that valiant army of the little brown Bees of Yamato.

COMMENTS ON THE STORY

The tale of Yogodagu and the Bees of Yamato is adapted, by kind permission of the publishers,

Messrs. A. and C. Black, from " How Yogodagu Won a Battle," contained in *Ancient Tales and Folklore of Japan*, by Richard Gordon Smith.

I have followed the outline of the original story, except as regards a detail or two of the climax. Actually, the Bees are said to have been housed in tubs and jars brought from neighbouring villages. And Yogodagu's men had increased from twenty to eighty men before the battle. It is a little difficult to explain why I felt it necessary to make the alteration ; it sounds absurd to say that I forsook the truth, in order to express it ! And yet, that is just what did happen.

The Bees are the chief actors in the story ; they are Yogodagu's true allies. And so I think they need to stand out clearly to the listeners, without a confused background of other helpers in the shape of friendly villagers and other reinforcements. Therefore, it seemed wise to keep the thread of the story as simple as possible, and not to suggest any intercourse with the world beyond the valley save for the one instance of the Messenger who brought the warning. This may seem a deal of explanation about a small matter ; but I think one should not alter the facts, as they stand, of any true or traditional story, without a good and sufficient reason ; so I am trying to make my reason clear.

I do not know that the introduction is necessary. I felt that the old rhyme makes a link between the children of England and the Bees of Japan. But one could equally well begin, " Once upon a time there was. . . ."

Description in stories should not, as a general rule, be long. The story-teller is apt to grow a little monotonous and the attention of the listeners may stray if there are too many details. But in this story the beauty of the valley needs to be clearly before us, and I think it is necessary to describe it at some length.

As far as the concluding battle is concerned, I have followed the excellent suggestion of Starveling the Tailor in *A Midsummer Night's Dream*. It will be remembered that the players are discussing the death of Pyramus, which it is feared may distress the ladies. " I believe," says Starveling, " we must leave out the killing when all is done." Most story-tellers will agree that this is good advice, when stories for children are in question. I do not mean that we are to shirk the subject of death. When it is necessary to meet and deal with it we must do so, wisely and fearlessly. But it is certainly not wise to fill children's minds with pictures of pain and terror for the sake of making a story more vivid or more "exciting"; and all that seems necessary here is to make it clear that the army of the enemy was utterly defeated.

I suppose that, to some extent, the story may quite well be true. There is a tale that some stout-hearted apprentices beat off a midnight attack on the town of Andernach, by hurling down hives of Bees upon the besiegers. Yogodagu and his men may have defended themselves in this fashion. Anyone who has dealt with Bees knows that an overturned hive is rather like a bursting bomb!

However, whether the tale is precisely true is not actually of great importance. What does matter is the spirit of the story; for therein speaks the mind of a nation, a mind so clearly attuned to gratitude for gifts received and services rendered that its songs and its stories continually harp upon that note. Yogodagu, even in his weariness and despair, is yet alive to, and thankful for, the surrounding beauty; the little Bee-man brings gratitude for help; his followers valiantly fulfil their leader's pledge. And Yogodagu's final act of remembrance is the crown of a very courteous and gracious tale of Old Japan.

The TALE of KING SOLOMON and the HOOPOE

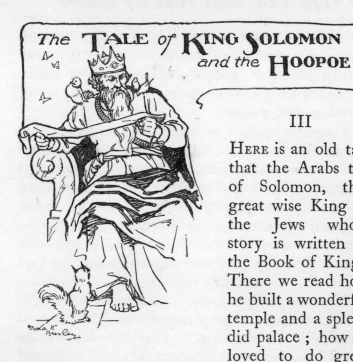

III

HERE is an old tale that the Arabs tell of Solomon, that great wise King of the Jews whose story is written in the Book of Kings. There we read how he built a wonderful temple and a splendid palace; how he loved to do great works and to send out his ships to gather rich and curious treasures. "Once in three years," says the story, "came the navy of Tharshish, bringing gold and silver, ivory, apes and peacocks." King Solomon wrote books of wise sayings; he made sweet songs to sing. And besides these, he wrote down all that he could learn of trees and plants, from the great cedar of Lebanon to the little green plants that grew between the stones of his palace walls ; and he gathered together all he could hear of beasts and of birds, of creeping things and of fishes. He loved to know all that could be known of everything that lived.

Now in the days of King Solomon very few people troubled themselves about those strange and lovely things, the wild plants and trees and creatures of this world of ours. We are beginning to love and understand them now, but it seemed very strange to the great King's people that he should trouble his head about such common things. And so I suppose when he found out and wrote down something no one had ever noticed, about some bird or beast or plant, men thought that he had learned it by magic ; and they looked at each other and said, " See how wise is the King ! He knows the language of all birds and beasts. The birds tell him where they build their nests and the beasts show him their hiding places. Even the tiny creeping ants have taught him where they store their winter food " (Proverbs xxx. 24–31). And they really thought that Solomon by his magic could talk to all creatures and make them do his will. They believed wonderful things of the King and his animal friends. Some of these tales are told to this very day. The story I am going to tell you is one of these. It is the story of King Solomon and the Hoopoe.

First of all, do you know what a Hoopoe is ? He is a bird ; a small bird with a long, sharp beak. He is rather bigger than a thrush, but he has longer and stronger legs than a thrush because he likes running better than flying. His wings and his tail are striped across with black and white. His head and his neck are a beautiful colour, almost golden ; I think they would look like old gold in the sunlight. And on his head— but I am not going to tell you what there is on his head. You must wait till the end of the story.

Well, one day King Solomon was riding in a wild and lonely place on the edge of the desert. What he was doing there I cannot say. Perhaps he had been talking to some of the chiefs of the desert tribes. Perhaps he had been visiting some town or village. Or perhaps he had only ridden out to watch some bird or beast or flower that grew in the desert country. And now he was on his way home, and he was very hot and tired. It was summer-time, and as the sun climbed higher and higher in the blue sky, its rays beat down upon the King till he longed to be in his palace in Jerusalem, with its cool, dark rooms and its splashing fountains. But Jerusalem was far away, and Solomon was almost fainting with the heat. He looked round for shelter ; but there

was no shade to be seen, not a tree, not even a great rock. There were only low prickly bushes, hot sand and pebbles, and patches of dusty ground covered with burnt-up grass.

Presently a great flock of birds came flying like a cloud across the desert. Just for a moment as the flock passed overhead its shadow fell upon King Solomon and gave a cool and pleasant shade as it covered him from the hot rays of the sun. The birds flew on ; their shadow skimmed over the ground beneath, and as Solomon watched it he said to himself : " I will call my friends the birds of the desert to help me." He looked round to see which of them was near ; and there quite close to him was the Hoopoe, pecking and scratching happily on a pebbly, sandy bit of ground. You and I might not have seen him at all, for his golden head and neck are very much the colour of golden sand in the hot bright sunshine, and his black and white wings and tail look wonderfully like a heap of stones and pebbles. But Solomon saw him in a moment, and he said : " Oh, little friend Hoopoe ! Call your brothers and bid them fly like a thick cloud between me and the sun that I may have shelter from the heat."

And the Hoopoe said : " Oh, Lord King, most certainly I will." And he gave his queer little cry that sounds like " Ooop-ooo, ooop-ooo," and called his friends. And they all came, and spreading their wings they flew between King Solomon and the sun, and they sheltered him from the heat. So the King rode on in comfort all through the long, hot hours of the day, till the shadows began to stretch out longer and longer, and he knew that the cool of the evening was near. And presently a little breeze began to blow, and he stopped his horse and called to the Hoopoes, " Come now, my friends, tell me, what shall I give to you, as thanks and a blessing for your great kindness to me this day ? "

As they heard his call, the Hoopoes wheeled in the air and came sweeping to the ground, and they folded their wings and sat round King

Solomon, and they all looked at the Hoopoe who had called them, as much as to say, " You speak for us," because they were rather shy. And the Hoopoe looked down at the ground and scratched bashfully with his little claws, because he was feeling shy too, about what he was going to say ;

and then he looked up at King Solomon and said :
" O Lord King, all the time that we have been
flying above you, we have admired the beautiful,
shining, golden crown that you wear upon your
head. Grant that henceforward all Hoopoes
may wear shining golden crowns like yours,
O King ! " (And I really don't wonder he was
bashful about asking, do you ?)

But King Solomon looked rather sadly at the
Hoopoe. " Little brother," he said, " is there
nothing else that will please you as well as a crown
of gold ? "

And the Hoopoe said, " *Nothing*, my Lord
King," very firmly, because you see he had quite
made up his mind and it was no use arguing
with him.

" Then you and all Hoopoes shall have golden
crowns," said the King ; and he raised his hand.
And immediately on the head of every Hoopoe
was a little shining, sparkling crown of gold,
most beautiful to see.

" But remember," said Solomon, " remember,
O little friends of mine, that your crowns may
bring you sorrow instead of joy. In seven days
from now I will come again to this place, and you
shall tell me if your wish is still the same."

But the Hoopoes scarcely listened to him ;

they were admiring each other so much. They could hardly wait to thank the King properly, before flying away helter-skelter to show all the other birds and beasts and insects how grand they were. And King Solomon watched them go and sighed a little, and rode back to his palace in Jerusalem.

The Hoopoe who had asked for the crowns flew home as fast as he could go. He wanted to get back to his wife, who was tucked away in a hollow tree, sitting on a nest full of eggs. She was hungry, poor thing, and rather cross, because she had been waiting all the afternoon to be fed. She poked her head out of a little hole in the tree trunk when she heard him coming, and was just beginning to scold him when she caught sight of his golden crown.

"Why, Father Hoopoe," she said, "what *is* that curious thing upon your head?"

"Don't you admire it, my dear?" said Father Hoopoe; and he told her all about his afternoon's work and how all Hoopoes had been given shining golden crowns by the great King.

"Have I got one on my head?" asked Mother Hoopoe.

"Yes, my love," said Father Hoopoe. "All our folk are wearing them now."

" Then I don't like it at all," said Mother Hoopoe. " It's not as comfortable as feathers. I wondered why my head felt so heavy. And besides that, Father Hoopoe, do you think it is *wise* to wear anything so bright ? "

" I don't know what you mean, my dear," said Father Hoopoe, crossly. " It is most beautiful and becoming. And now, do let me get a wink of sleep. I am too tired to talk any more, after all that flying."

But at the bottom of his heart he was not quite so sure as he had been that a golden crown was really the best thing for a little bird to wear. And when morning came and he went out to peck and scratch for food, he soon found that Mother Hoopoe was right. As I told you, his feathers had been exactly the thing to hide him ; they were so much the colour of the sand and stones that he could hardly be seen. But a shining golden crown is very easy to see in the sunlight, and poor Father Hoopoe had never had so many narrow escapes as on that day. Hawks swooped down at him, and he had to hide among thorn bushes. A jackal pounced at him, and he only just fluttered away in time. And worst of all, a shepherd boy with a sling chased him with stones wherever he went. He had very hard work to find enough food for Mother Hoopoe and himself, and by evening he was very tired and miserable. All his friends were unhappy, too, and the next day it was worse. Folk with slings and sticks and stones seemed to be everywhere. The shepherd boy had spread the news of the birds with the golden crowns, and from far and near men came to hunt them down.

Fortunately, Mother Hoopoe and her nest were well hidden away, deep in the hollow tree, so she was safe. But she was nearly starved, poor thing; Father Hoopoe scarcely dared show the tip of his long beak to look for food.

At last the evening of the seventh day came. " And now, my dear," said Mother Hoopoe, " do go and ask the King to take the nasty things off our heads and let us have a little peace. I have hardly had a wink of sleep for worrying about you, and it is time we both had a little more food."

And poor, tired Father Hoopoe said in a weak voice, " Yes, my love ; I certainly will."

He flew away to the place where he had last seen King Solomon. There sat the great King on his horse waiting, and from far and near Hoopoes came flying to meet him. Their golden crowns shone in the sunlight, but their feathers were draggled and ruffled, and there were not

62

nearly so many Hoopoes as before. I am afraid the men with slings and sticks and stones could have told the reason why.

King Solomon looked at them sadly. " O little friends," he said, " are you happy with your crowns ? "

And all the Hoopoes answered together : " Take away our golden crowns, O King ! take away our golden crowns ! "

And Solomon said, " I will. Crowns of gold are not for birds to wear. But because you are the friends of a King, and gave him help in time of need, every one of you shall wear the crown of a King, but it shall be of feathers, not of gold."

And he raised his hand. The Hoopoes looked at each other, and on every Hoopoe's head was a little crown of feathers, gold-coloured, and tipped with black.

And this time they really thanked King Solomon properly. They pattered round him on the sand ; they bowed and scraped and piped their little call of " Ooop-oo, ooop-oo," again and again. They thanked him in every way they knew. And the wise King smiled and blessed them and sent them away to their homes.

Father Hoopoe flew straight back to Mother Hoopoe. She popped her head (with a dear little

63

feather crown on it) out of the hollow tree when she heard him coming.   And when she saw him, she was perfectly delighted.   " My dear love,"

she said, " *how* charming, *how* distinguished, and what *very* good taste."

" Yes, m y dear," said Father Hoopoe, " and *so* safe ! "   And he flew happily away to find some food for himself and Mother Hoopoe before the sun went down.

And now you know what the Hoopoe wears upon his head ; and don't you think King Solomon was kind ?

COMMENTS ON THE STORY

There are stories without number of King Solomon ; as Mr. Kipling tells us in the prelude to " The Butterfly that Stamped " ("Just-so

Stories "), " there are three hundred and fifty-five stories about Suleiman-bin-Daoud " (and it will be remembered that he names as one of these the tale of " The Hoopoe that shaded Suleiman-bin-Daoud from the heat ").

The great King seems to have stamped his memory deep upon the imagination of the East. And who can wonder that reads of his doings, in the Book of Kings and Chronicles ? There is the marvel of the Temple that he builded of marble and cedar and gold. There is the record of the House of the Forest of Lebanon, with its throne of ivory guarded by lions of gold, its shields and targets of beaten gold, its drinking vessels, " all were of gold ; none were of silver, it was nothing accounted of in the days of Solomon." Read of the navy of Tharshish, with its fairy-tale merchandise, " gold and silver, ivory and apes and peacocks " ; of the Queen of Sheba, with her splendid gifts and her innumerable questions and testings of the great King's understanding ; of the kings who brought tribute, of how " all the earth sought to Solomon to hear his wisdom." Was ever fairy tale so wonderful ; was ever pageant more splendid ? We seem to have strayed from the story of the Chosen People, the worshippers of the One God, into some strange tale of the Arabian Nights. Even the chronicler seems dazzled as he writes. And as we read we can well understand how legends would be born as the wonders of the great King's reign passed from mouth to mouth and from age to age.

Something of this I have tried to show in the introduction to the story, founded on 1 Kings iv. 31–34, 1 Kings x., and Proverbs xxx. 24–31. (I hope all who read will refresh their memory— if needful—from these references !) I felt that before telling the story I wanted the children to understand that we are not dealing with just a fable or a fairy tale ; we are dealing with a legend. I wanted them to see how legends come to be, and to realise that there can be truth in them since they arise out of the impressions that a great man, or a great event, has made upon the mind of mankind. Legends may not be true according to facts, but they may well be true in spirit. They grow out of truth and often help to express it.

Some of us have scruples about telling children such stories—we are afraid of puzzling or mis-leading. But if we approach them quite simply and plainly by the road I have suggested here, I think we may feel that we are only helping to a fuller understanding. St. George fought no dragon, it is true, but he left a memory of such noble and undaunted courage that to future generations it seemed that dealing with dragons was all in his day's work. It is not very likely that St. Patrick sent the serpents trundling out of Ireland like so many hoops ; but his wisdom and his wit met and overcame so many subtleties of evil that it is small wonder it was afterwards told of him that he could dispose of venomous snakes. And to those who heard tell of the great King, his riches, his magnificence, his wisdom and the curious learning that led him to write of trees, " from the cedar tree that is in Lebanon even unto the hyssop that springeth out of the wall," and " of beasts, of fowls, of all creeping things and of fishes," it seemed but a small thing that Solomon should deck the Hoopoe with its little feathery crown.

There is a beautiful group of Hoopoes in the Natural History Section of the Victoria and Albert Museum, South Kensington, London. Father Hoopoe is there with his crest outspread. Mother Hoopoe peeps out of a hollow tree (she has folded back her little crown). And down below the tree trunk is sawn apart to show the nest with six or eight baby Hoopoes (poor innocents), fluffy, half-fledged, and golden-crowned.

The Hoopoe is, I believe, sometimes met with in England. He is, or used to be, among our native birds, but he has become very rare, and I am afraid his life is precarious. For his little crested head is unmistakable, and we have an odd way of expressing our delight in meeting a rarity : whether it be bird, beast or insect, flower or fern, we promptly do our best to " collect " it and convert it from a lovely living thing into a " specimen." (I am not referring to collections in museums, but to the indiscretions of the amateur collector.) If King Solomon had known of this habit, I think he would have left the Hoopoe without its feathery crown.

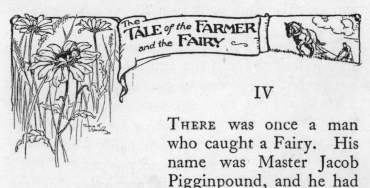

The TALE of the FARMER and the FAIRY

IV

THERE was once a man who caught a Fairy. His name was Master Jacob Pigginpound, and he had a little farm and a little house where he lived with his wife, Mistress Martha Pigginpound. Early in the morning, one day in June, Master Jacob went out to the pasture to drive the cows in for milking, and there, right in the middle of an ox-eye daisy and fast asleep, lay the Fairy! He had been dancing all night on a fairy ring, and he was so tired that he had climbed up the stalk of the daisy and had laid himself down to rest a little, and, as I said, he had fallen fast asleep on its yellow middle.

Some people would have thought it was a lovely thing to find a Fairy—wouldn't you? But Master Jacob only thought of what he could get ; and he picked up the poor Fairy between his big finger and thumb and carried him into the house —still half asleep. And he said, " Wife, I've caught a Fairy!" Mistress Martha begged him to let the Fairy go among the flowers in the garden. "Put the poor little dear in the red rose bush, or among the pinks, or into a Canterbury bell, Jacob, do," she said. But Master Jacob shook his head.

And he fetched a big blue and white mug and popped the Fairy in and said, "There you shall stay till I hear what you'll give me to let you go." And he put a saucer on the top and stood the mug on the kitchen dresser. Mistress Martha didn't dare to touch it; she knew Master Jacob would be angry if she meddled. So there the poor Fairy had to stay all that day, and out of doors the sun shone, the birds sang, and the tall white daisies, the buttercups and the grass and the red sorrel nodded and danced as the wind blew over the hayfields.

In the evening when Master Jacob had finished

his day's work and had come home to get his tea, he lifted the saucer off the mug and said, " Well, Master Fairy, what is it to be ? " And the Fairy said in a small, clear voice, " You shall find a piece of gold at the end of every furrow that you plough " ; and then he jumped—just like a grasshopper, very quick and sudden—straight out of the mug, right over Master Jacob's head, on to the window-ledge and out of the kitchen window into Mistress Martha's bed of pinks that grew just outside the house. " And a good thing too, poor little creature," said Mistress Martha.

But Jacob said nothing at all. He forgot all about his tea ; he was out of the house in a minute, and he harnessed a horse to the plough and drove a furrow right down the middle of the pasture field where the cows were feeding. And sure enough, at the end of the furrow there lay a shining gold piece ! He went on ploughing till the moon was high in the sky, and by that time half the green pasture field was turned to brown furrows and Master Jacob had a pocket full of gold pieces.

After that Jacob did nothing but plough, and as soon as his fields were ploughed, he ploughed them again. Nothing grew on his farm, for he neither planted nor sowed, he only picked up gold pieces and stored them away. He sold his cows, he ploughed up his garden, his pastures and his cornfields. He grew thin and bent and weary with ploughing. He was afraid his gold would be stolen, so he never spoke to his neighbours, and he let no one come near the house. And he could never bear to spend his precious gold, so he and poor Mistress Martha had scarcely enough to eat.

So the time passed and June came round again, and one day Mistress Martha stood at the door of the house looking out at the little farm. She shook her head and almost cried as she looked. The garden was gone; there were no more pinks or roses or Canterbury bells. There were no lavender bushes, no vegetable garden, with tidy green rows of carrots and potatoes and peas. The green grass was gone too, so were the hay-fields and the fields of clover and young green corn. There was nothing to be seen but bare brown earth, and in the distance she could see Master Jacob toiling after a plough and stooping at the end of each furrow to pick up his piece of gold.

" Bless the man ! " said Mistress Martha, " there he goes—working all day and half the night, and bags of gold in the house, and both of

us just as miserable as can be ! I wish we could go back to last June, so I do, so happy and comfortable as we were ! "

Just at that moment Mistress Martha heard a loud cackling behind the house, and then another hen joined in with more loud cackling. " I do believe those hens have been laying," she said. " I don't know what's been wrong with them lately, I've had no eggs at all. I'll go and see." She bustled round to the hen-house and came back again with two beautiful big brown eggs. " I do declare," she said, " I'll boil these eggs for tea. A new-laid egg will be a treat and do us good. So it will."

She stood by the door watching for a moment with the two brown eggs in her hand. Just as she turned to go into the house the garden gate clicked and a little lame old man with a pedlar's pack upon his back came hobbling up the path.

73

"Wherever did he come from?" Mistress Martha said to herself. "I never saw him coming up the road; I suppose the sun was in my eyes."

"It's no use your coming here," she said to the Pedlar. "I've no money to spend on ribbons or laces—or needles and pins and tapes either, for that matter, nowadays."

"Let me rest a minute, mistress," said the little old man. "I'm old and the pack is heavy. Could you spare me a drink of water? It's a hot day and the road is dusty."

"Sit down on the step," said Mistress Martha, "and let your pack down to rest your back. You shall have the water and welcome." She fetched the water, all cool and fresh from the well, in the same blue and white mug that Master Jacob had put the Fairy in. And then, because the Pedlar looked so old and tired, she stepped back into the kitchen and took the brown egg that she was going to have for her own tea and laid it carefully in the pack, all among the pink and blue ribbons and the handkerchiefs and laces. "There you are," she said, "I wish I had more to give."

"Thank you, mistress," said the old man, "with all my heart. One good turn, they say, deserves another ; so take a dip from my lucky bag before I go." He held out a little bag that looked as if all the colours of the rainbow had been woven into it—as green as grass, as red as poppies in the corn, as yellow as buttercups and as blue as the summer sky, with every colour you can think of in between. Mistress Martha put her fingers in, but all she could feel was a soft powdery stuff.

"Take a pinch and smell it," said the little old man. So Mistress Martha sniffed. It was so sweet that she shut her eyes to smell it better. "It's like the pinks that used to grow under the kitchen window," she said. She sniffed again. "No—it's like the lavender bushes that grew by the garden path." She sniffed again. "It's like the big red rose bush that grew by the gate," she said, and sniffed again, a very big sniff. I think she was going to say, "It's like mint and thyme and sage and southernwood," but she never said any of it. She only sneezed. "A-t-choo," said Mistress Martha, "A-t-choo— a-*tish*-oo."

She shut her eyes tighter than ever when she sneezed—most people do. And when she opened them, the Pedlar was gone. But Mistress Martha had no time to be surprised at that, she was so busy looking with all her eyes. For what do you think? It *was* the pinks under the kitchen window that were smelling so sweet; and it *was* the lavender bushes with their grey-green leaves and blue-grey flowers; and it *was* the big red rose bush that grew by the gate. There they all were, and all the other flowers too, and there were the mint and thyme and southernwood, the carrots and turnips and potatoes and peas. Mistress Martha rubbed her eyes and looked, and then she looked again. The pasture was there, and so were the cows; in the field beyond the young green wheat was growing, and she could see the hayfield rippling in the wind. And there was Master Jacob coming whistling up the road, just as he used to come before he found the Fairy and shut it up in the blue and white mug.

"Bless me!" said Mistress Martha, and she turned round and looked in at the kitchen window; there was a beautiful tea on the table—a currant loaf, white bread and brown bread, yellow butter and creamy cheese, and streaky pink and white bacon. The kettle was boiling on the fire and the big brown teapot was standing on the hob. "Bless *me*," said Mistress Martha, and she ran upstairs and looked in the box under the bed. The bags of gold were gone! There was only Master Jacob's big leather purse with the money for market day.

The queerest thing of all was that when Master Jacob came in and washed himself and sat down to his tea, he seemed to have forgotten all about the Fairy and the fairy gold. He ate his tea and enjoyed it, and then he said, " Wife—we'll go to market to-morrow and buy you a new dress. You look a bit tired, and a change will do you good." And when they got to market everybody else had forgotten about  Master Jacob's ploughing and his unneighbourly ways too. Mistress Martha had a new dress of a beautiful blue, just like periwinkle flowers, and she felt so happy and excited about it that she began to forget as well. And quite soon the only person who remembered was the Fairy. He was very careful never to go to sleep in the middle of an ox-eye daisy again !

And who do *you* think the Pedlar was ?

COMMENTS ON THE STORY

There really was a Farmer who drove a bargain with a Fairy, so at least old chronicles say. It is told how one, Johann Wilde, of Rodenkerchen (the tale is Scandinavian), captured a "little one" and received as ransom "a plough that would leave a gold ducat in every furrow. . . . The Farmer ploughed and never ceased ploughing till he wore himself to death, all alone, for he suffered none to come a-nigh him. His only thought was how he might plough more swiftly."

On this dismal tale of greed and its retribution I have founded the story of Master Jacob and his Fairy. I have used only part of the original story and have told it rather briefly as a prelude. One might almost look on it as the memory that is in Mistress Martha's mind as she looks at the disconsolate little farm. It needs to be told, I think, much as one tells the events that led up to a surprising experience—clearly, but as a reminiscence. It is not to be lingered over—we are collecting the facts and explaining how things came about.

Then comes the second part, and now there are pictures to be seen and watched as we tell. The poor, bare, brown fields and garden in the June sunshine, under the blue June sky ; Mistress Martha standing at her doorway looking sadly at it all ; bustling to the hen-house and returning with her two brown eggs ; the old Pedlar with his wrinkled face and his wise, fairy eyes. And then Mistress Martha and her pinch of fairy dust. Remember, we *are* Mistress Martha when we come to that ; like her we forget the Pedlar, the empty fields and the bare garden ; we are looking with " the mind's eye " at all the sweetness of those vanished flowers. And after that terrific sneeze (which needs some practice) we, too, come back to find the garden really there. We see it—gay and bright with all its flowers—and beyond it lie once more the pastures, the blue-green of the young wheat, and the woven rippling carpet of the hayfields—green and yellow and red and white, with dusty purple bloom of tall meadow grass powdering softly over all.

Then we survey that beautiful tea and hurry upstairs with Mistress Martha to look for the fairy gold. More and more it is as if we are awakening to reality after an ugly dream, till finally we go with Mistress Martha and Master Jacob to market. And with friends and neighbourly gossip and the glory of the periwinkle-blue dress, the nightmare really vanishes quite away. I could not feel that, in telling the story for children, it was necessary to bring Master Jacob to a miserable end. It seemed enough to give a glimpse of the ugly things that greed can do, and then to let the kindness of Mistress Martha and the Fairy repair the dreary prospect.

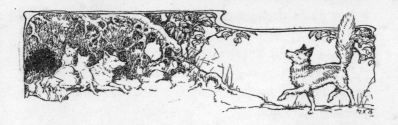

V

THE BATTLE OF THE BIRDS AND THE BEASTS

LONG, long ago, an old story says, the Wren was made king over all the birds, because though he was so small he was very clever. And this is the tale of the great battle between the birds and the beasts that was fought in his reign and what came of it.

It was a lovely summer day. The sun was shining, the sky was blue, with big soft white clouds ; the trees of the forest waved gently in the wind. And Mother Fox was lying stretched out in the sunshine, in front of the burrow where she and Father Fox and their four fox cubs lived. The cubs were playing games, jumping over her, chasing each other and tumbling over and over on the ground. Mother Fox watched them and blinked in the sunshine.

F 81

Just then there was a little rustle in the bushes, and Father Fox trotted up. He looked very important and very much pleased with himself.

" There is going to be a battle ; and *I* am to be general," said Father Fox, very loudly and grandly.

The cubs were making so much noise that Mother Fox could not hear him very well. Besides, she was sleepy. So she only blinked her eyes and said, " What, dear ? " in a kind voice. Father Fox said it again in a louder and grander voice. " There is going to be a battle, and they have chosen *me* as general."

This time Mother Fox really did hear, and she was very much surprised. She sat up suddenly, and the cubs, who had been climbing on to her, rolled over and over to the ground. " Bless me ! My love ! " said Mother Fox. " A battle ! Who is going to fight, and what are they fighting about ? "

" My dear," said Father Fox, " you are so busy with the children nowadays that it is not surprising that you never hear anything except their chatter. I must tell you that those ridiculous creatures, the birds, have been making a great fuss over nothing at all this week."

" What was it all about ? " asked Mother Fox,

giving a little pat to the biggest cub who was biting his brother's tail.

"Do attend to *me*, my dear, and leave the children alone for a moment," said Father Fox. "It all came of something Cousin Bear said when he came to spend the day with Cousin Wolf. It seems that Cousin Wolf showed him the Wren's nest and told him the Wren was king of the birds. And Cousin Bear peeped in and saw the ridiculous little baby Wrens with no feathers on ; and he laughed and roared till he had to lie down and roll on the ground, because his sides ached so with

laughing at the royal children who were so ugly. And when Father and Mother Wren came home and heard about it they were very angry."

"Quite right too," said Mother Fox. "*I* should be angry if anyone laughed at *my* children."

"Pray do not interrupt me, my dear," said Father Fox. "I quite agree with Cousin Bear. And now those foolish little creatures, the birds,

83

say that unless the Bear says he is sorry they will fight us. So there is to be a battle—the birds against the beasts—and *I am to be general.* I shall hold my beautiful bushy tail high in the air, and all the beasts will follow me. As long as I hold my tail in the air they will march forward and fight. It will be a glorious victory!" said Father Fox.

"I am sure I hope so, dear," said Mother Fox. "But how are you going to fight creatures that can fly in the air, when you can only walk on the ground?"

"Do not be silly, my love," said Father Fox.

But he could not think of an answer just at the moment, so he trotted away.

Mother Fox lay down again, and the fox cubs began their games once more. They jumped over her and climbed on to her and rolled off again, while she blinked in the sunshine.

"It is no use talking to Father Fox," she said to herself. "But I don't know what he will do if a bird flies up and pecks his nose!" But not even Mother Fox guessed what was really going to happen.

Father Fox had gone back to the edge of the forest where all the beasts were holding a council of war. There was a great noise, and everyone was talking and laughing at once. They had just heard that all the other creatures with wings had joined the birds. The Bees, and the Wasps, the Hornets (who are like very big Wasps), the Beetles (who have wings tucked away under their horny coats), the Butterflies, the Dragon-flies, the Mosquitoes, the Midges, and the Gnats, and a whole host of other little flies—all were getting ready for war. And, though the beasts did not know it, the smallest of the Gnats had been sitting under a leaf, all the time they were making their plans. He was listening to every word they said !

Presently, just about sunset, he flew away to tell Father Wren what he had heard. "The Fox is to be general," said the Gnat. "He will march first holding his tail in the air. As long as he holds his tail up all the beasts will follow him wherever he goes."

Father Wren's little black eyes twinkled as he listened. He nodded his little brown head. "Send the Wasp to me," he said. So the Gnat flew away and presently a Wasp came flying up. Father Wren whispered something to him. (And what it was you shall hear later.) The Wasp gave a loud "B–z–z–z–z," which was his way of saying "Yes," and flew off to his nest for the night.

85

And Father Wren put his head
under his little brown wing, while Mother
Wren kept the Wren babies warm, and they
all slept soundly till it began to grow light next
morning.

The battle was fixed for mid-day, and by that
time the army of the beasts was all ready, with
Father Fox marching proudly up and down,
waving his beautiful tail. The branches of the
trees were full of birds ; the Wasps, Hornets
and Gnats, the Midges, the Beetles and Butterflies, and all the other flies, fluttered and hummed
and buzzed loudly round. And just at twelve
o'clock (when the shadows are shortest and the
sunshine is hottest), Father Wren gave a loud
chirp, and Father Fox cried proudly, " Forward
march ! " and the battle began.

The birds rose in the air like a cloud. The
Flies and Wasps and Bees and Hornets and Gnats
buzzed louder than ever. And the beasts, with
Father Fox in front of them, marched steadily on.

No doubt it would have been a very grand

battle, but almost as soon as the march began something happened to Father Fox. He gave a loud squeaky bark and jumped high into the air ; and then he jumped again and then again. He ran round in circles chasing his tail and yelping loudly. The beasts stood still and watched him in surprise. And then—down went his beautiful tail just as low as it could possibly go, and Father Fox turned and ran as if he was running for his life, shrieking loudly all the time ! And the Hare, who is always easily frightened, suddenly said, " Dearie me, dearie me, dearie, dearie me ! " and began to run too ; and in another minute all the beasts were running as fast as they could go. And they never stopped till they were safe at home in their dens and holes and burrows. The battle was over and the birds had won.

But what was the matter with Father Fox ? Well, Father Fox ran and ran and ran till he tumbled through the bushes that grew in front

of his burrow, and almost fell over Mother Fox, who was lying blinking in the sun with the four fox cubs playing round her. She looked very much surprised to see Father Fox coming home in such a hurry, because, of course, she thought he was leading the army.

But before she could speak Father Fox squealed, "There is something in my tail. Take it out ! *Take it out* ! ! TAKE IT OUT ! ! !" And then with a loud buz-z-z-z-z a big black and yellow Wasp flew out of poor Father Fox's tail just where it was thickest and fluffiest. He had been sitting there stinging Father Fox. Do you wonder poor Father Fox felt uncomfortable and couldn't hold up his beautiful tail !

So that was why the battle ended without any fighting at all, which was a very good thing. And of course as the beasts were beaten they had to send the Bear to say he was sorry for being so rude to the baby Wrens. And I think that was a very good thing, too—don't you?

COMMENTS ON THE STORY

Most story-tellers know the prelude to this tale, telling how once the birds assembled to choose a king. He who could fly highest was to become their ruler. The contest was held and the Lark, the Swallow, the Pigeon, the Wild Goose, and the Swan all rose to great heights, but far above all climbed the Eagle. At last, even he could go no higher, and he was preparing to descend when up from his back there rose a tiny brown speck and mounted higher still. It was the Wren, who had hidden himself among the Eagle's feathers and had been carried upon those powerful wings.

And so, since no one could deny that the Wren had risen highest of all, he became the king of the birds.

I suppose no theme is more beloved of the folk-tale (I should say, of the generations which made and told the folk-tale) than that which tells of " the weak things of the world " confounding " those things which are mighty." It is not surprising, since such stories usually have their origin among the folk of some small community which is at the mercy of a grasping overlord, terrorised by a powerful neighbour or preyed upon by robbers.

Both tales of the Wren's stratagems are good examples of the type. But Father Wren's device has the merit of being quite legitimate ; there is no suspicion of sharp practice about it (which is more than can be said for the shorter story).

The original tale is one of Grimm's. I have amplified the portrait of the Fox and have made him a conceited fellow, in order to sharpen the contrast between the small winged creatures and their big, blustering opponents. Father Fox is very puffed up, from the moment he appears upon the scene. He speaks in a lofty, condescending voice to Mother Fox who, he feels, is a homely person quite ignorant of the really important news of the world. Mother Fox is quite calm, not ruffled or perturbed. She is used to his ways and knows more than he does really, though she does not show it.

I have been rather puzzled, from a realistic point of view, as to how Cousin Bear managed to see the baby Wrens. Wrens build as a rule, I believe, in some hollow or crevice, usually with a very small opening for safety's sake. I have known them build in a hole in a haystack, among the stones in a rock-garden, or in a hole in a gate-post. No human eye could peep into the tiny doorway and see the unfledged Wrens, but perhaps Cousin Bear's eyes were keener sighted. It seems a small point, but it is not so in principle. For the story-teller must be sure of his ground, must be honestly convinced that the way is clear. The story must be real and true while it lasts, and it cannot be either if we are uneasily conscious of a gap in our defences, of a happening which cannot be accounted for. Besides, a story is not merely words. The words form and suggest pictures. And if the picture in the story-teller's mind is blurred and uncertain, the story will lose in clearness ; it will not be convincing. And lastly, children have a way of suddenly enquiring into details. One should be prepared, as far as possible, with a reasonable answer.

The end of the story, with the defeat of the army and the flight of Father Fox, needs a little extra preparation. The catastrophe should not be hurried or confused. The picture must be sharp and clear ; the dignified start ; Father Fox's sudden stop, his agitated jumps and yelps, and his headlong flight—all should be really seen in the mind of the story-teller. We pause a moment with the astonished army, and then comes the Hare's panic and the utter confusion and dismay of the beasts.

We shall probably need to practise " Take it out ! *Take it out* ! ! Take it out ! ! ! " It need not be very loud, but it must be full of feeling. Father Fox cannot bear that thing in his tail a moment longer.

91

Last of all we tell, with comfortable content, the Bear's apology. The story is finished, the Wrens are appeased, the boaster is ridiculed, and Cousin Bear has made amends. It is a tidy and satisfactory ending.

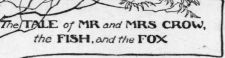

VI

Mr. and Mrs. Crow sat on the branch of a tall tree that grew by the side of the river. They both looked very cross; their feathers were ruffled, their tails drooped, but their little beady black eyes were very bright and wide awake. They were watching a fisherman in his boat. By and by they knew he would come to land with his load of fish, and if he had caught a good many that morning he would throw away some of the smallest, and that would make a good breakfast for Mr. and Mrs. Crow. But he had been there since five o'clock, when the sun rose, and so had they, and now it was ten o'clock, which is a long time to wait for your breakfast. So perhaps it is no wonder they were feeling cross.

" I *wish* he would come to land ! " said Mrs. Crow in a peevish voice.

" So you have said several times already," said Mr. Crow, very grumpily. " I wish you

93

would be quiet. Each time you say it, it makes me feel emptier."

"Well," said Mrs. Crow still more peevishly, "I am sure I don't care . . ." But she was interrupted (perhaps it was a good thing) by a loud "Caw! Caw!" from Mr. Crow. "Look! Look!" said Mr. Crow, "he is coming to land."

The fisherman had turned his boat and was rowing slowly in to the bank. Mr. and Mrs. Crow could see that the big rush basket in the bottom of the boat was quite full of silvery, shining fish.

"There is sure to be plenty for us," said Mr. Crow. He was so excited that he nodded his grey head and flapped his wings and did a little dance on the bough of the tree. This time it was Mrs. Crow who said crossly, "Do keep quiet. If you make such a fuss you will have every crow for miles and miles coming to see what there is to eat." They were certainly in a very bad temper that morning!

But when the fisherman came to land he did not throw away a single fish. "A very good catch this morning, and all fine fish," he said to himself. "I shall take them all straight to market." And he tied up his boat, lifted his heavy basket of fish,

climbed up the river bank and went away by the
path that led to the town.

Poor Mr. and Mrs. Crow were terribly disappointed and they felt hungrier and emptier
than ever as they saw all those beautiful fish
being carried away from them.   But the basket
was very full and as the fisherman hurried along
a large fish slipped from the top of the load and
fell among the bushes and long grass that grew
by the side of the path.   The fisherman did not
notice it ; he went on his way and was soon out
of sight.   Mr. Crow did not see it either, he
was looking at the fisherman's boat to see if there
was not a scrap of food or something to eat—even
a bit of leather would be better than nothing, he
thought.

But Mrs. Crow was watching the fisherman
with her sharp, black
eyes.   She saw the
fish fall and she spread
her black wings and
swooped down to look
for it.   Mr. Crow
turned his head as he
saw her move and fol-
lowed her like a flash
to see what she had

95

found. She was trying to drag the fish from among the bushes, but it was too heavy for her. Mr. Crow's strong beak and claw did most of the work, and soon the fish was lying on the short grass by the river bank, ready to make them a splendid breakfast.

And I expect you are thinking that they each said "Caw! Caw! Caw!" in comfortable, contented voices, and ate till they were hungry no longer? That is what sensible crows would have done certainly, but Mr. and Mrs. Crow were cross, and when people are cross they are very often not sensible at all. So instead of beginning to eat, they began to quarrel about whom the fish belonged to!

"I saw it first," said Mrs. Crow; "it is *my* fish."

"You are quite wrong," cawed Mr. Crow. "I dragged it out of the bushes —it is *my* fish."

"It *isn't*!" shrieked Mrs. Crow.

"It *is*!" croaked Mr. Crow.

They flapped their wings and danced on their grey toes; they snapped their beaks and talked so loudly that a Fox who was creeping through the bushes to see what he could find to eat, heard them and came to see what all the noise was about.

"Dear Mr. and Mrs. Crow," he said politely, "pray tell me what is troubling you so."

And Mr. and Mrs. Crow both screamed at once and each told him how greedy and selfish the other was.

The Fox listened with a twinkle in his eye, and when they had finished he said, still more politely: "Dear friends, let me help you. I will divide the fish, so that each of you shall have a fair share."

Now if Mr. and Mrs. Crow had not been so cross I think they would have remembered that the Fox liked fish quite as much as they did. But they were too angry with each other to think of that. They cawed "Yes" in croaky, grumpy voices, and the Fox bit the fish in two with his sharp white teeth. (He took a very good mouthful too, as he did it.)

"You have very good taste in fish.

G

97

This is most delicious, dear Mr. and Mrs. Crow," he said.

"Caw! caw!" said Mr. and Mrs. Crow in a great hurry to begin.

"But wait a moment," said the Fox; "I see that one piece is a little larger than the other. I must just put that right." And he took a large bit from one half of the fish and then stepped back and looked at it again with his head on one side.

"Dear me!" he said, "*this* is too large now— that will never do." And he took a mouthful from the other half and looked again.

"How stupid of me," he said, "I cannot get them equal." And he took another bit from the first half.

"Oh dear! oh dear!" said the Fox, looking at the second half, "now *that* is certainly the bigger." And he swallowed so much of it that only a small piece of the tail was left.

Poor Mr. and Mrs. Crow were so surprised to see what was happening that they could not say a word (and to tell you the truth, I think they were a little afraid of the Fox, with his long nose and sharp, white teeth). But when they saw how little was left of their beautiful fish they found their voices.

"Stop! *Stop*! S<small>TOP</small>!" they cawed, "go away, you thief, and leave the rest to us!"

But the Fox only looked at them, and his eyes twinkled more than ever. "*Think* of all the trouble I have taken to divide the fish properly for you," he said. "I will just take this mouthful for payment, and that will make it right." And he bit off all the rest of the fish and only left the head!

"Good morning, dear Mr. and Mrs. Crow,"

said the Fox. "I am sure you have each got quite a fair share." And he trotted away through the bushes and left Mr. and Mrs. Crow looking at the head and the tail.

I am afraid they had a very small breakfast that day! Poor, cross Mr. and Mrs. Crow, I feel very sorry for them, don't you?

C<small>OMMENTS ON THE</small> S<small>TORY</small>

There are several versions of this tale, which is a very old one. Æsop tells it twice. In one variant two men find an oyster, and disputing its possession, are left with a shell apiece, the contents being swallowed by the man to whom they had appealed. In the other, two cats quarrel over the division of a piece of cheese, which a monkey nibbles away, as the Fox does the fish. There is also an Indian version, on which I have founded the story of Mr. and Mrs. Crow.

This might be described as a " cautionary " tale, and I think, with all such, that we need to remember that they are to be looked on first and foremost as *stories*—not as a moral dose to be administered or a disciplinary stick to be shaken in the faces of our listeners. Our business as story-tellers is *to tell a good story*, and to tell it in such whole-hearted fashion that while the story lasts we and the children are all living in the little scene which it sets out for us. We follow the action ; we watch the pictures. We sympathise with poor hungry Mr. and Mrs. Crow, we feel sorry for their greediness and bad temper (*sorry*, not superior, because, alas ! we are so often like Mr. and Mrs. Crow when things go wrong). We laugh over the sly villainy of the Fox, and are left lamenting with the unfortunate pair. And if we succeed in making the story a living thing, if we and the children are all interested together, the

" moral " may safely be left to take care of itself. Our listeners will understand without words— which is the best kind of understanding—that the crows brought their sorrows very largely upon themselves.

The dealings of the Fox with the fish are, of course, the very pith and marrow of the story, and the success of this part depends on its being made very clear and easy to follow. The Fox does not hurry, nor must we. He is smooth and deliberate and sweet-tongued. " Hm-m-m," he seems to say, as he stands back and surveys his work with half-closed eyes, and then steps forward and adjusts matters with a rapid mouthful. A turn of the head, a slight gesture of the hand, will show which " half " he is attending to. We see it all as we tell, stage by stage, till the sad finale comes with Mr. and Mrs. Crow gloomily gazing at the melancholy remnants of that beautiful fish which would have made such a banquet if they had been content to share it in amity.

THE TALE of the HARVEST BUN

VII

ONCE upon a time there was a mother and she was baking harvest buns. Do you know what a harvest bun is? Just in case you don't, I had better tell you. A harvest bun is something like bread, but it has currants in it, and sugar in it, and candied peel in it, and spice in it. And when it has been baked and comes out of the oven it looks like a big brown bun; and you can't think how good it smells, and, unless you have eaten harvest buns, you can't possibly tell how good it tastes!

Well, as I said, the mother was baking harvest buns. Next day the corn was to be cut—everybody would be busy and everybody would be hungry—so the oven was full and they smelled delicious. The father sniffed and the children sniffed (they were a boy and a girl), and they all thought, " How good they will taste to-morrow."

Presently the mother opened the oven door, peeped in, and said, " The bun on the top shelf is beginning to burn. I had better take it out." And she pulled out the baking tin and I think it burnt her hand, for she gave a little squeak and nearly dropped the tin, and out bounced the harvest bun and down to the floor it fell. And would you believe it ! Instead of lying there flat upon the floor it gave a hop and a skip and jump and began to roll towards the door. And out of the door it went, singing to itself :

> " *I'm a harvest bun,*
> *I'm a curranty bun,*
> *And I roll and run,*
> *I roll and I run.*
> *The father and mother,*
> *The sister and brother,*
> *They* ALL *run after the harvest bun.*"

And when they had stopped being too surprised to move, so they did ; and you can't think how fast they ran, but they *couldn't* catch up with the harvest bun.

Well—as the bun rolled through the farmyard it met a duck, and the duck looked at the bun with her little black eye and thought how nice it would be to eat (and so it would), and she said, " Quack ! quack ! Where are you going ? " But the bun never stopped. It didn't want to be eaten by a duck, so it rolled on faster and faster, singing to itself :

> " *I'm a harvest bun,*
> *I'm a curranty bun,*
> *And I roll and run,*
> *I roll and I run.*
> *The father and mother,*
> *The sister and brother,*
> *The duck makes another,*
> *They* ALL *run after the harvest bun.*"

And so they did, and the duck waddled after, but they *couldn't* catch up with the harvest bun.

Well, as the bun rolled out of the farmyard gate it met a hen, and the hen looked at the bun with her head on one side and she thought it looked very nice to eat (and so it did), and she said, " Cluck ! cluck ! Where are you going ? " But the bun never stopped. It didn't want to be eaten by a hen, so it rolled on faster and faster, singing to itself :

> " *I'm a harvest bun,*
> *I'm a curranty bun,*
> *And I roll and run,*
> *I roll and I run.*
> *The father and mother,*
> *The sister and brother,*
> *The duck makes another,*
> *The hen flaps above her,*
> *They* ALL *run after the harvest bun.*"

And so they did, and the hen flapped along and cackled (hens do fly when they are very excited), but they *couldn't* catch up with the harvest bun.

Well, the bun rolled out of the farmyard into a lane, and there it met Old-Man-John hobbling along. And Old-Man-John looked at it and he thought it looked very nice and brown (and it certainly was), and he said, " Hullo ! hullo ! Where are you going ? " But the bun never stopped. It didn't want to be eaten by Old-Man-John, so it rolled on faster and faster, singing to itself :

> " *I'm a harvest bun,*
> *I'm a curranty bun,*
> *And I roll and run,*
> *I roll and I run.*
> *The father and mother,*
> *The sister and brother,*
> *The duck makes another,*
> *The hen flaps above her,*
> *And Old-Man-John*
> *Comes hurrying on,*
> *They* ALL *run after the harvest bun.*"

And so they did, and Old-Man-John came hobbling behind, but they *couldn't* catch up with the harvest bun.

Well—the bun went rolling down the lane and there it met a horse. And the horse thought it smelled very nice (and it really did), and he said, " Clip-clop ! Where are you going ? " But the bun never stopped. It didn't want to be eaten by a horse, so it rolled on faster and faster, singing to itself :

> " *I'm a harvest bun,*
> *I'm a curranty bun,*
> *And I roll and run,*
> *I roll and I run.*

> *The father and mother,*
> *The sister and brother,*
> *The duck makes another,*
> *The hen flaps above her,*
> *And Old-Man-John*
> *Comes hurrying on,*
> *And the horse trots along,*
> *They* ALL *run after the harvest bun."*

And so they did, with the horse trotting in front, but they *couldn't* catch up with the harvest bun.

Well—as the bun rolled by a field of grass a cow looked over the hedge, and she thought it a beautiful bun (and so it was), and she said, " Moo, moo ! Where are you going ? " But the bun never stopped. It didn't want to be eaten by a cow, so it rolled on faster and faster, singing to itself :

> *" I'm a harvest bun,*
> *I'm a curranty bun,*
> *And I roll and run,*
> *I roll and I run,*
> *The father and mother,*
> *The sister and brother,*
> *The duck makes another,*
> *The hen flaps above her,*

And Old-Man-John
Comes hurrying on,
And the horse trots along,
The cow says, " Moo ! "
And she's coming too,
They ALL *run after the harvest bun."*

And so they did, with the cow mooing behind, but they *couldn't* catch up with the harvest bun.

Well—the harvest bun came to the bottom of the lane, and it rolled round a corner, and there was the river. The harvest bun didn't know what to do ; nobody could roll upon a river you know. But just then, up trotted a fine fat pig. And when the fine fat pig saw the harvest bun he thought it looked beautiful and plump and brown (and so it did), and he said, " Humph, humph ! What are you doing *here* ? " And the harvest bun, who was really rather tired of rolling, said in a very quiet voice :

" I'm a harvest bun,
And I'm not very big,
Please carry me over,
Dear Mr. Pig."

And the pig said, " Of *course* I will. Jump on my back."

108

So the harvest bun gave a hop and a skip and it jumped on to the pig's back.

And the pig said, " The water is very deep, I think you'd better come up higher."

So the harvest bun gave a hop and a skip and it jumped on to the pig's head.

And the pig said, " The water is very wet, I think you'd better come *inside*." And he tossed

" I'm a Harvest Bun and I'm not very big   Please carry me over dear Mr Pig "

up his head and he caught the harvest bun in his mouth and gobbled it up, and went splashing across the river. And I don't suppose the harvest bun minded at all, do you? because harvest buns are made to be eaten, and he was a nice, fat, comfortable pig.

And the father and mother, the sister and brother, the duck and the hen and Old-Man-John, and the horse and the cow all came round the corner just in time to see the fine, fat pig gobble up the harvest bun. So they all turned round and went home again. The horse and the cow went back to their fields, and the rest went back to the farm, and Old-Man-John went too. And all the other harvest buns were baked and brown; so next day when the corn was cut everyone had harvest buns for lunch and tea.

And don't you wish you had one too? I do!

COMMENTS ON THE STORY

Probably most readers of this story will recognise it as one more version of the tale which is so well known already under the various guises of "The Johnny Cake," "The Gingerbread Man," and "The Pancake." (The last-named, a Norwegian folk tale, is, I think, the original from which the others have grown.)

Very possibly those who usually tell the tale in any of the fore-mentioned versions, and also the children who are accustomed to it, will prefer to keep to their old friend. But there may be some to whom the tale is quite new, and there may be others who will like this home-made variant because, like myself, they have found it hard to make the cake *run* when he did not *rhyme*. I confess to having been unable to put any " go " into the other versions for that reason, excellent stories though they are.

So I have put the old tale into a new dress, and feel a certain satisfaction in it because it pays a tribute to the memory of the kind Welsh cook who first taught a small ten-year-old person the spicy delights of harvest buns.

How delightful they are must be clearly understood between story-teller and listener as a preliminary to the story. " It has *currants* in it—and *sugar* in it—and *candid peel* in it—and SPICE in it," we say impressively and suggestively (and one small listener that I know nods his head after each with deep satisfaction).

The rhyme is a jingle, but must never degenerate into a sing-song. The harvest bun is full of lively satisfaction and so must we be. Each addition to the train of followers brings a fresh picture into view, and if we watch the story as it goes and see all clearly, I think no difficulty will be found in remembering the rhyme. Clear visualisation is a wonderful help to memory. I am quite sure that we story-tellers should set ourselves to " see " our stories far more definitely than we usually do. It is no mere words but living pictures that we need to have in mind as we tell.

The final episode needs practice. It is not quite easy to suddenly " switch " from the smooth swift rhythm that tells how " they couldn't catch up with the harvest bun," into the more ordinary tone of the conversation with the pig. If we are not careful, we shall sound jerky or flat. I think this part needs to go rather slowly and clearly— and very cheerfully. It is not a sad ending, but a most friendly disposal of the harvest bun.

Then rapidly (but never gabbling) we finish the tale and send all the pursuers comfortably home.

The Tale of TIMOTHY TITTLEBAT & THOMAS TINKLER

VIII

ONCE upon a time there were two old men. Their names were Timothy Tittlebat and Thomas Tinkler, and they lived in a little hut on the edge of a forest. A few miles away was a village, and there Timothy went to sell wood, and to buy bread and butter and cheese. Thomas never went, he was far too lazy. He sat outside the hut in the sunshine on fine summer days and watched the hens pecking and scratching, and once in a while if a hen cackled he went to look for an egg. On wet days and cold days he sat by the fire.

Timothy did the work. Timothy dug the garden and the little field of corn. Timothy planted the cabbages and hoed the carrots and onions. Timothy went to the forest with Peter Longears, the little grey donkey, and Jacky Feathertoes, the little brown dog, to bring back

H

the logs to sell and to burn. He was busy all day long, and he whistled and sang as he worked, while Thomas sat comfortably at home and grumbled and growled. (I feel sorry for Thomas, don't you? He must have been very dull.) Timothy was sorry for him too. "He was badly brought up," he used to say. "If Thomas had been taught to say ' please ' and ' thank you ' when he was a little boy, he'd be a deal better tempered now."

Timothy was fond of Thomas, although he was so cross. Nobody else was fond of him, and nobody cared to come to the little hut to talk to him, so if it had not been for Timothy he would have been very lonely indeed. Even Peter Long-ears and Jacky Feathertoes kept out of his way as much as possible. But they loved Timothy and trotted after him and helped him all they could. Peter carried loads of wood and Jacky caught rabbits and laid them at his feet, as if to say, "There's a dinner for you."

Timothy and Thomas had lived together for a great many years, and now they were growing old. Timothy's back ached at the end of a long day's work, his legs didn't walk as fast as they used to do, and his arms got tired with chopping wood. Peter Longears was old too, and couldn't carry such big loads, and Jacky Feathertoes was getting too stiff to run about and catch rabbits.

"Whatever will Thomas do," Timothy used to say, "when we all get too old to work ?" And Peter and Jacky would look at him solemnly as much as to say, "We really do *not* know."

The year this story happened, the autumn was warm and dry. September passed, October came. Every day the sky was blue, and the sunshine was golden, and the forest grew more beautiful day by day. The dark green leaves of the oaks turned to golden-brown. The beeches were red-brown, yellow and amber colour. The hazels shone golden-green, and all along the edge of the forest the rose-hips, the brambles, the dogwood, and hawthorn trees were scarlet and orange and crimson.

But though the days were fine and warm, the nights were cold and frosty. Thomas grumbled as he sat over the fire in the evenings, because the logs were small and gave so little heat. It was all Timothy could do to cut enough wood to sell, and the best logs had to be loaded on to Peter Longears' back to take to the village to buy bread and cheese. But he was sorry for Thomas, and when the last day of October came (which, as everyone knows, is called Hallowe'en),

Timothy said to himself, " There's that bough of the great oak that fell in the storm last year. I'll go to-day and chop it up and bring back a log or two for Thomas. He shall have a good fire for Hallowe'en, bless his heart ! "

So when he had finished his day's work he took Peter Longears and set off through the forest, with Jacky Feathertoes trotting behind.

The sun had nearly set ; only the edge of it showed like the rim of a great red ball in a bank of blue mist, but the full moon was rising, very large and round and orange-golden, so Timothy knew there would be plenty of light. It was some way to the place where the old oak grew, and he was tired. So were Peter Longears and Jacky Feathertoes ; they had all three been to the village with a big load of wood that day. But they trudged steadily on till they came to the tree. It stood all by itself in a little open space and round it the grass grew green and soft, with tufts of heather and sprays of gold-brown bracken and little star-shaped yellow flowers here and there. A great bough had fallen and lay all across the green. Timothy took his axe and began to chop, while Peter Longears nibbled and munched and Jacky Feathertoes sniffed among the bushes.

Timothy was very tired ; he could only chop

slowly and the wood was tough. It seemed hard work to cut through the thick bough ; but he thought of Thomas and his Hallowe'en fire, and went patiently on till quite a little pile of logs was ready.

" That's as much as Peter can carry," said Timothy, " so we'll be going home." He loaded the logs on to Peter's back and was turning to go when he noticed a little pool of water that shone in the moonlight, just at the edge of the shadow of the great oak.

" I never noticed that pool before," he said. " How did it come here, with such a dry autumn and no rain for weeks ? But a drink of water will do me good. I do feel *that* tired ! "

He led Peter Longears to the pool and knelt down and drank. It was the most wonderful water, so clear and fresh and cold.

" I do declare," said Timothy, " it makes me feel as if I could dance all the way home, instead of creeping along with a stiff back."

Peter Longears and Jacky Feathertoes had their noses in the pool by that time, and they seemed to like the water too. They drank and drank, and suddenly Peter lifted up his head and brayed. " Eh-haw ! Eh-haw ! Eh-haw—aw—aw—aw," said Peter Longears, and he kicked up his heels and *pranced*. He stood on his hind legs, he stood on his fore legs, he almost stood on his head ; and Jacky Feathertoes flew round and round him in circles, barking at the top of his voice.

" Bless me ! " said Timothy, scratching his head in surprise, " what has come to my old Peter and Jacky ? There's something very odd about them both ! " And then it struck him that there was something very odd about him too, for he could feel that his head was covered with thick curly hair—and

Timothy Tittlebat was nearly *bald*. He looked down at the little pool—the water was as clear and shining as a looking-glass in the moonlight—and it was not poor, tired old Timothy that he could see there, but a young, strong Timothy, with a brown face and bright blue eyes, and curly brown hair. And when he looked at Peter Longears and Jacky Feathertoes he

saw that they, too, were young and strong and
sleek.

" Why ! " said Timothy, " this must be a fairy
pool. Come along, Peter ! Come along, Jacky !
We must go and bring Thomas to drink of it too."

He jumped on to Peter's strong back (because
four legs can go faster than two), and they went
galloping down the
wood-way, with Jacky
Feathertoes barking
beside them.

Thomas came hob-
bling out to meet
them, very cross, be-
cause his fire was
burning low and there
were no more logs.
It took some time to
make him understand what had happened, and
that it was really Timothy who was talking to
him. But as soon as he did understand he
scrambled on to Peter's back.

" I can go by myself," he said. " I won't
have you coming along and drinking up all the
water. You've had your share, and now I shall
have mine." Timothy didn't try to argue about
it. Thomas always did just what he liked, and

Peter and Jacky could find their way, and they would take care of him. So he let them go and they trotted away up the path. Timothy watched for a moment and then turned towards the hut to get supper ready. But first he chopped up a big log that lay by the door. It had been too thick and heavy for poor old Timothy Tittlebat, but it seemed nothing at all to strong young Timothy. Then he piled up the fire, set out the bread and cheese, and put some new-laid eggs ready to boil, swept out the hut and stood waiting at the door to see Thomas come galloping home.

But though he waited and waited, no Thomas came. There was not a sound in the forest, not a breath of wind or a leaf stirring. The full moon lit up the wood-way and Timothy listened and looked, but he could hear nothing and see nothing but the shadows of the trees lying dark in the moonlight. He wondered where Thomas could be.

Presently, after a long while, he heard the sound of Peter Longears' trotting feet. "Here they come," he said to himself. "How pleased Thomas will be! He'll be hungry too, and cold maybe," said Timothy, and he turned to make up the fire and put on the eggs to boil. But when he came to the door again and looked, it was only Peter Longears and Jacky Feathertoes who came out of the forest. Thomas was not there ! They looked at Timothy—talking with their eyes as animals do if they love you—and said quite plainly, " Come and see." Timothy jumped on Peter's back, and off they went as fast as their legs could go. They galloped along the path and into the clearing where the great oak grew. Peter stopped short to let Timothy get down, and Jacky trotted across to where the little pool had been. There was no clear water shining in the moonlight now, but only a tiny hollow of bright green moss, with little yellow star-shaped flowers growing round it. And by the side of the hollow lay—what do you think ? By the side of it lay Thomas Tinkler's old clothes, and half in and half out of them the nicest baby you could possibly see—just about a year old, fat and rosy, blue-eyed and golden-haired ! And when he saw Timothy he kicked and crowed, and Timothy ran and picked him up and said, " Bless me, Thomas, it's never you ! " *But it was.*

You see, Thomas was always greedy, sad to say, and he was determined to drink all he could get of the fairy pool. So he drank and drank till he had finished it all, never thinking that too

121

much of a good thing might be good for nothing, as the saying goes ; and of course after that he grew younger and younger till he stopped at one year old.

So Timothy and Peter Longears and Jacky Feathertoes took Thomas home. They  could not really feel very sorry, for he had been such a crotchety, cross old man, and this was such a nice baby. Timothy took great care of him, and it was not long before there was somebody else to take care of him too. For young Timothy Tittlebat fell in love with a very nice young woman in the village, and she fell in love with him. So they were married, and they brought up Thomas Tinkler so kindly and carefully that he really turned out very well indeed, and they all lived happily for many years after.

As for the fairy pool, no one ever saw it again, but the place where it lay is still quite plain—a little hollow, as round as a ring, of fresh green grass and bright green moss, with little yellow flowers growing all about it.

COMMENTS ON THE STORY

The thought of living water which should restore vanished youth has always been dear to the wistful imagination of mankind. Folk-lore is full of tales concerning it. Sometimes it is called the fountain of youth, sometimes the water of life ; usually it is a spring, and I do not remember having encountered it as a still pool save in the Japanese story on which this tale is based.

In this original, a poor woodcutter and his wife drink. The wife, in her anxiety to become extremely young and lovely, drinks too much, and is transformed to a very small baby. The version I found was extremely short, but I suspect that if the story were told at length she would prove to be a jealous shrew. Woodcutters in fairy tales are frequently unhappily wed (though I can see no reason why they should be), and the wife's shortcomings would provide an element of justice which otherwise seems lacking.

I replaced the woodcutter and his wife by Timothy and Thomas, partly because such a pair —even if one be grumpy and selfish—is more wholesome to contemplate than a quarrelsome husband and wife. But my main reason for making the change was that Thomas, as a baby, is not only funny and surprising ; he is also easy to provide with a future satisfactory to all concerned. A wife of one year old seems to complicate life for her husband, however rejuvenated he may be.

This point might not occur to our listeners, but it would probably trouble ourselves. We should not be content with such an ending as that of the original. It seems neither happy nor appropriate. And unless we story-tellers can feel that a story is going to be " well and truly " ended, we lack the complete conviction that is necessary to whole-hearted telling. Story-telling is story-sharing, and the close of the story should bring satisfaction to teller and listeners alike.

A TALE of GOOD-LUCK and MRS FEATHERFUSS

IX

HAVE you ever heard someone say, "I had Good Luck to-day," or "Good Luck came my way to-day," or perhaps, "I met with Good Luck to-day"? It all sounds rather as if "Good Luck" was a kind of person, and something like that is what people used to believe. There are all kinds of stories of how "Good Luck" came, and here is one of them.

Once upon a time, many years ago, old Mrs. Featherfuss was standing at her garden gate. She was a large, stout person with white hair and a very clean white apron. The house behind her was very clean and white too. The stones of her garden path were as white as stones could possibly be, and so were the palings of her garden. It was a very tidy garden. There were no flowers in it, but there was a row of parsley down each side of the path, and there were neat rows of vegetables —carrots, with feathery tops turning red and golden-yellow, dark crimson beetroot, stout green cabbages, and shining celery. Old Mrs. Featherfuss looked as if she liked good things to eat, and so she did. She was thinking, as she stood there, of the little black pig in the sty at the back of her house—how fat he was growing and how good he would taste with sage and onions and apple sauce !

" But I mustn't stand here wasting time," she said to herself ; " I must go and make up the fire and see about my tea."

Just as she was turning from the gate an old Beggar Man came hobbling down the road. He seemed very lame and very tired. Old Mrs. Featherfuss hurried up the path for fear he should ask for something. " I've got enough to do to look after myself," said she. The Beggar stopped a moment and leaned against the palings as if he would like a rest, but Mrs. Featherfuss bustled round the corner of her house and into the kitchen by the back door. She shut the door with a very loud slam and began to poke up her fire to boil the kettle to make a cup of tea. The Beggar Man shook his head and sighed and went on down the road.

There was another house a little farther on— a very tiny one. It had a thatched roof that came low down, just like a comfortable old hat pulled over somebody's head. A rose bush grew on one side of the door and a red fuchsia on the other ; they almost hid the front of the tiny house, and its little windows peeped out like two bright eyes. There was a cabbage patch on one side of the garden path, and on the other side there were flowers—Michaelmas daisies, buttony brown chrysanthemums, and pink and blue asters.

As the Beggar came down the road an old woman in a blue-checked apron came out of the little house. Her name was Betsy Pinkpottle and she lived there all alone, with her big tabby cat for company. She had a face that was all brown and rosy and wrinkled like a little old apple, and brown eyes that twinkled very kindly. The Beggar Man looked at her and nodded his head as if he saw something pleasant. " Good evening, missus," he said. "Could you spare a poor old man a bit of bread and cheese?"

Betsy's eyes twinkled more than ever. "I can give you something better than that," she said. "I've got no cheese, but what would you say to a fine large rosy apple? I had three beautiful ones given to me to-day. I was just going to have one for my tea, and you're welcome to one too—indeed you are."

She trotted into the kitchen and came out again with a large red apple and a big slice of bread on a blue and white plate. The Beggar Man thanked her and settled down on an old tree trunk by the side of the road to eat. Presently he came to the door: it was standing wide open, and Betsy was sitting at the table finishing her tea. "Here's the plate, missus," said he, "my thanks to you, and may what you begin at sunset go on till moon-time, without stop or stay!" And he went hobbling down the road. Betsy came to the door and stood watching him and wondering what he meant.

"The sun is setting, sure enough," she said to herself, "but there's nought to be done but tidy the kitchen. What should I be doing till moon-time?"

She stepped back into the house and picked up

the apple that was left and put it on the shelf. Then she turned again to clear away the tea things. But there was still an apple on the table. " Bless me ! " said Betsy, " where did that come from ? " It was large and round and red and shining. Betsy felt it ; it was certainly a real apple, and as it was on her kitchen table it must certainly belong to her, so she put it on the shelf beside the other. They looked very nice sitting there, and Betsy admired them with her head on one side. And when she turned round there

was another apple on the table in the very same place—a beautiful streaky red and yellow one. " Well I never *did*," said Betsy, and she picked it up and put it by the side of the other two. " Three lovely apples," she said, and so they were. And then she looked, and there was a fourth all ready for her, just as round and as

I 129

rosy as the other three, and after that another and another. Betsy went on for a whole hour taking apples off the table and putting them on her kitchen shelves. There were rows and rows of them, and her arm was really beginning to ache, when at last she turned round and found no apple on the table.

"Well there!" said Betsy, "that's the last. Where they came from I don't understand, but a beautiful lot of apples they are."

And then she thought of the Beggar Man's saying, "May what you begin at sunset go on till moon-time." She opened the door and looked out; and there, low down in the sky, was the tiniest and newest new moon that was ever seen. Betsy dropped three curtseys to it, as her grandmother had taught her. "From sunset to moon-time," she said. "They must have come from the Beggar Man. Good Luck has surely come my way to-day!"

The next morning Betsy Pinkpottle was busy trotting round to all her neighbours, giving a red apple here and another one there and telling the tale of the wonderful Beggar. Everyone said, "Well, you did have Good Luck yesterday, I'm sure!" and everyone was pleased except old Mrs. Featherfuss. She was very angry. "To think," she said, "that I saw him coming down the road and never asked him in. Well," said Mrs. Featherfuss, " if he comes this way again he shall come to me and I'll get something better than a lot of apples, I'll be bound." So every afternoon she stood at her garden gate, with her clean white apron on, waiting for the lame Beggar to come down the road. And one day, about two weeks later, he came.

Mrs. Featherfuss bustled out to meet him and invited him to come in and take something to eat. She hurried him up the path and in at the front door, and sat him down in the best armchair in the parlour. Then she gave him plum cake, and bread and cheese, and bread and butter, and bread and jam, and a mug of cider to drink. And she sat by him and thought what a large meal he was eating, and counted up in her mind all she hoped to get in return. Presently he got up to go. Mrs. Featherfuss showed him politely to the door and there he said, "Thank you, mistress. Good evening to you, and may what you begin at sunset go on till moon-time, with never a stop nor stay." And he hobbled down the path and away.

Old Mrs. Featherfuss turned back into the house. It was just sunset. "I must be quick," she said ; "there's not much time before moon-rise. It's a good thing I put the money ready." (There was a fat bag of shillings and sixpences, half-crowns and florins, standing on the table.) "All I need to do is just to open it and pour out the silver. It will go on pouring out till moon-rise, and I shall be a rich woman by that time ! "

It was a beautiful plan and perhaps it would have succeeded quite well if she had not upset the jug of cider in her hurry to seize the bag. "Dear, dear," said Mrs. Featherfuss, "what a terrible mess ! " She snatched up a cloth and began to mop up the cider. There seemed to be a great deal of it. "I never thought that jug held so much," she said. She wiped and mopped, and still the cider dripped and poured on to the par-lour floor. She ran and fetched another cloth and a pail from the kitchen. The parlour floor seemed to be swimming in cider by the time she got back ; the carpet was soaked, and there was a stream running down the passage into the kitchen. " Dear, dear, *dear* ! What a terrible mess ! " said old Mrs. Featherfuss. She put the pail by the table to catch the cider and ran back to the kitchen to fetch her long-handled mop. And just as she got there the cider stopped running, and old Mrs. Featherfuss, with the mop in her hand and a very red face, stood staring through the kitchen window at a large round full moon that was just rising out of a bank of grey mist beyond the fields and hedges.

" From sunset to moon-time ! " she said, " and all I've got is a spoiled parlour carpet and a pailful of cider ! "

And that was all she ever did get. It took her most of the night to clean up the house, and the parlour carpet was never quite the same again.

COMMENTS ON THE STORY

The story of " Good Luck and Mrs. Feather-fuss " is founded on one of the many folk tales which tell how opportunity—in the guise of king or beggar man, wise man, fool, imp or fairy, as the case may be—knocks at the door of mankind and brings a blessing or a curse according to the reception that is accorded.

The original—from which this story has strayed rather far—is a Chinese tale of Fu-chen, the God of Happiness, who took the form of a lame beggar and asked alms at the house of a rich farmer. The farmer and his wife drove the beggar from their door ; but a poor widow took him in, gave him her own supper, clothed him with the linen laid by for her burial, and received a blessing as he departed : " May what you begin at dawn continue till sunset." She began to fold her remnant of linen at dawn and by sunset had innumerable yards laid by to sell. The farmer and his wife heard of the miracle, invited the beggar to their house, fed and clothed him sumptuously, and received the same parting word. They hurried to their strong box to count out gold, but instead spent the day brushing away cobwebs which they had allowed to accumulate upon it.

I felt that something more cheerful might be substituted for grave-linen, in a story for children ; also I could not feel convinced that so greedy a couple would ever allow cobwebs to gather over their money box—and a story-teller must be convinced or the story goes haltingly. These details being supplied, the story persisted on taking to itself an English setting, and I was forced to let it unwind as it wished. The " period "—if any—is Victorian, I suppose ; so tea-time, though unusual in fairy tales, is in order, and so are fuchsias and chrysanthemums in Betsy Pinkpottle's garden.

The descriptions of the gardens are necessary, I think. They form backgrounds for the owners, and once clearly visualised are not difficult to remember. " Seeing is believing " is as true in story-telling as it is in fact, and it is the best road to remembering. Neither should Betsy and her apples be hurried over ; we should find them, and enjoy them, one by one with her. Let us remember as we go that we must not only *tell* the story and *watch* the story, but we must also *be* the people in the story. Betsy, kind and cheerful—then a little puzzled—and again happily surprised and understanding. Mrs. Featherfuss, scheming and planning, giving only as a usurer gives that she may get thereby, waiting in acute suspense till the valediction is spoken. (I think we may go rather slowly at this point so that our listeners may be in suspense also.) And then crisp and clear come the details of the final catastrophe, which should be clearly visualised so that there is no halt in the telling. We leave Mrs. Featherfuss " sent empty away," bewailing her vanished hopes and her parlour carpet, which was " never quite the same again."

One point more : by way of forestalling possible criticism, I should like to point out that I have been very careful about the moon ! It is " moon-time " not " moon-rise," and Betsy's moon was a young moon, newly visible, but setting, low down in the west. Mrs. Featherfuss's moon was a full moon, just rising in the east. This makes times and seasons work out correctly, since even in a fairy tale one should treat the laws of the universe with respect !

THE CAT THAT CLIMBED THE CHRISTMAS TREE

X

A TRUE TALE

THERE was once a little girl whose name was
Elizabeth Ann. Her home was an old grey
house in an old grey town in the South of England—a big house with wide steps and pillars
before the door. When you opened the door
there was a square hall, with a great stove to keep
it warm in winter time. On the walls of the hall,
on three sides, were glass cases with stuffed birds
in them—great hawks and owls, and even a black
swan which Elizabeth Ann thought very queer

and interesting—and above them were stags' horns. On the fourth side there was a wide stone staircase that led to the upper part of the house. There were long passages and a great many rooms, and at the other end of the house there was a wooden staircase that was always called "the back-stairs." On wet days in holiday time the house was a lovely place to play "I spy," and "Hide-and-seek," and an exciting game called "Mother Bunch." You raced up the front stairs and along the passages and down the back stairs, and nobody seemed to mind how much noise you made.

There were plenty of people to play, too, for Elizabeth Ann had three sisters and two brothers, and there were always cousins as well, whose fathers and mothers were away in India or America or China. One Christmas Day there were seventeen boys and girls, and Elizabeth Ann's father and mother made nineteen people altogether, and they stretched right across the road and the pavements too when they went to church that morning.

So you see they needed a very large Christmas Tree. It seemed a very tall tree to Elizabeth Ann, and I think it really was, for her father always had to climb high up the big step-ladder to fasten the shining silver star to the top of the tree and to arrange the long chains of gold and silver paper, and set the little coloured candles on the upper branches. And while he was busy high up, the tall people helped a little lower down, and the people who were not so tall a little lower still. Everyone used to be busy with the Christmas Tree, and when it was finished on Christmas Eve it looked most beautiful.

It stood right in the middle of the hall, and it sparkled and shone. There were bright threads of gold and silver ; there were bags of sweets and flags and candles of all colours ; there were tiny looking-glasses and shining coloured balls among its branches. And Elizabeth Ann and all her cousins and sisters and brothers knew that on the next day there would be presents hanging there too. They went to bed so excited that they could hardly sleep.

But I have not yet told you anything of the person that this story is really about. Perhaps you will say that he was not a person at all, for he was a *Cat*. But everyone loved him so much that he seemed quite like a person. He was a large fluffy grey Cat, and his name was Mr. B. (He was so like an old gentleman with a fluffy grey beard whom Elizabeth Ann knew, whose

name began with a B, that nobody could help
calling him " Mr. B," though it does seem a very
odd name for a Cat !)

All through the winter Mr. B. was very fond of
lying by the stove in the hall. It was so warm
and comfortable and the garden and the shrub-
bery and the paths and the field, where he walked
in summer, were cold and wet for his fluffy feet.
So Mr. B. was there with everybody else on
Christmas Eve while the Christmas Tree was
being dressed, and I suppose he thought about
it and wondered in his fluffy grey head what
kind of shining things they were that hung
upon its branches.

Well, Christmas Day came, and everyone went
to church in the morning, and Mr. B. and the
Christmas Tree were left alone in the hall
with the nice warm stove. It was very cold
and frosty out-of-doors, and I am sure Mr. B.
was glad to be warm and comfortable, but I
think he must still have been puzzling about the
Christmas Tree. Perhaps, instead of lying by the
stove, he walked round and round and looked at it.
Nobody was there to see except the stuffed birds
with their shiny glass eyes, and if they did see him
they never told anyone about it. Presently
everyone came in from church, and they had

dinner, and Mr. B. had some too. (He used to have a little chair to himself at dinner time by the side of Elizabeth Ann's father, but he had his *real* dinner afterwards.)

By and by, when dinner was over and afternoon came, everyone went to finish tying up the presents before bringing them down to put them on the Christmas Tree. Mr. B. was left all alone in the hall again, and I suppose he felt that he really *must* find out about that curious tree. And what do you think he did? He got up and stretched himself, he came over to the Christmas Tree, he got on to the big pot that held it, and he began to climb! Nobody knows what he expected to find. Could it have been a mouse, do you think? Or did he think birds lived at the top of a Christmas Tree? Up and up he went—very slowly because the boughs were thick—pushing his fluffy grey head between the twigs and sniffing at the queer smell of candles and flags and sweets. And the farther up he went the less he

141

liked it. He wanted to come down, but there seemed so many things in the way. He was afraid to jump for fear he should be tangled in the gold and silver chains of paper and the shining gold and silver threads. And at last he felt he really could go no farther, and poor Mr. B. began to cry "Mee-e-ow! Mee-e-ow-e-e-ow!"

Everyone was busy, as I told you, tying up parcels, but Mr. B. cried so loud that Elizabeth Ann heard him, and she said, "What is the matter with Mr. B.?" and somebody else said, "What *is* the matter with Mr. B.?" and somebody else said, "*What* is the matter with Mr. B.?" and somebody else said, "What is the matter with *Mr. B.*?" and they all came out of the different rooms where they were wrapping up presents and came down the staircase all together, all looking for Mr. B. And they could hear Mr. B. saying, " Me-e-ow, Mee-e-e-ow, E-ow-ow," very loudly and most sorrowfully, but no one could see him. The hall was dark, but there was a nice red glimmer from the stove, and they could see he wasn't lying there. They lit the gas and looked, and they couldn't see him anywhere in the hall ; and then they looked at the Christmas Tree and there he was ! There he was like a fluffy grey caterpillar, quite high up the tree, holding on very tightly and calling for  help with all his might. Poor frightened Mr. B. !

So Elizabeth Ann's father got the tallest step-ladder and set it by the Christmas Tree and climbed up and took hold of Mr. B. and gently pulled away his little grey paws that were clinging so tightly to the tree, and said, " Poor Pussy."

And Mr. B. climbed on to father's shoulder and took hold of it with all his claws, and came riding down the step-ladder safe and sound, and he jumped down and shook himself, and sat down by the stove and washed himself all over because he didn't like the smell of Christmas Tree !

But everyone else went back and finished wrapping up the presents, and put them on the tree, and under the tree, and round the tree ; and then they all had tea and Christmas cake. And afterwards they lit all the candles and danced round the Christmas Tree and sang, " Here we go round the Christmas Tree," to the tune of " Here we go round the Mulberry bush." Mr. B. sat by the stove and watched them all. He never climbed a Christmas Tree again. He knew everything that he wanted to know about Christmas Trees you see !

COMMENTS ON THE STORY

I think the chief merit of " The Cat that climbed the Christmas Tree " is that it really happened. Largely on that account it was always a great favourite with play-centre children. So I have written it down here in the hope that others—and especially little children—may like it too.

I often think that, since most of us have some such stories laid by amongst our reminiscences of childhood, it is a pity that we do not use them more. We are apt to think of them as if they were disjointed fragments, " fossil remains " of a past age. They need, of course, to be thought over and put into shape for telling. They must have their background and setting made clear ; we must recall and tell the little things that are so familiar to us that we do not realise how delightful they are to our small listeners. And we can do this ; our memories are not so poor and our childhood is not so far past, but that we can look back to happy days of sunshine or warm, homely firelight, and in the glow of these our stories will stand clear and live. The things that so delighted us are the very things that other children will delight to hear.

It may be that—as in the case of " The Cat that climbed the Christmas Tree "—there is very little action in some of these stories. I do not think that greatly matters where small children are concerned. Older children, like ourselves, desire a plot. They demand that the stage should be set, the action begun, and that something should come of it. There should be some just and inevitable conclusion, whether it be in the form of a dramatic climax or one of the safe and comfortable variety. But the small child loves chiefly to watch pictures go by—something pleasant, something friendly and familiar—with just a little current of action to carry the story along.

So I think this story should go leisurely and comfortably on its way, with due regard to its details and repetitions. We, like Mr. B., are deeply interested in that Christmas Tree, and we do not mind how often we are recalled to look at all its shining splendours.

XI

I T was a very cold day, just about the time of the
New Year. The sun shone brightly, but the
north wind blew cold over the moor, and hurried
ragged white clouds across a pale blue sky ; and
as the day went on the clouds came thicker and
heavier, till there was scarcely any blue sky
left.

"Snow before morning—snow before morning!" said old Mother Jennifer to herself as
she sat spinning brown sheep's wool into yarn for
stockings, at the door of her little house. It was
a very tiny house, tucked away under a hill,
built of grey stones piled together, with moss and

heather stuffed between them to keep out wind and rain. The roof was of boughs covered with turf and flat stones, and it almost looked like part of the hill except for the smoke that curled out of its chimney. But it was warm and weather-tight, and if you had peeped inside you would have seen that there was a good fire on the hearth, and all along one wall were piled turf and tough old twisted roots for burning. There was room in the little house for Mother Jennifer and her family, and that was all that mattered. The family were close beside her as she sat and spun. There was a nanny-goat nibbling grass, two hens —one brown and one speckled—and a little black cat was washing himself by the warm hearth. They were very good company Mother Jennifer thought, and she talked to herself and to them most of the day.

Every now and again she looked up and down the road that ran across the moor to see if anyone was in sight. It was a long straight road—as straight as if it had been ruled with a ruler. The Romans had made it long before Mother Jennifer's time, and it ran over hill and dale without a bend or a turning and dropped down into the hollow where the stream flowed and the village lay, and then it climbed the farther hill and stretched away and away to the Great Wall that the Romans built. There the road is still, and you can see it and travel on it if ever you cross the moorland. But there was no sign of anyone upon it that day, and old Mother Jennifer was troubled. " The miller's man should have been here by now," she said, " with the bag of meal. There's not much left in the meal chest, and if it snows deep to-night we shall all be hungry here before the roads are clear again."

She stayed by the door watching till the sun went down in the west and shone out under a bank of heavy grey clouds with one last blaze of red light that made the heather and bracken look as though they were lit by the glow of a great fire. Then she went inside and shut the door and stirred the turf on the hearth and put on a piece of wood to make a blaze. Nanny the goat came too, and Speckle and Brownie the hens. Nanny lay down by the turf pile ; Speckle and Brownie fluttered to the top of it ; and the little black cat stretched himself and looked round and yawned till his little tongue looked like a curly pink feather, and blinked his eyes at Mother Jennifer as much as to say, " Here we are, all snug and warm together, this cold winter's night."

Mother Jennifer sat down by the fire and went on spinning. Presently she looked up. " Is it the wind," she said, " that whistles so loudly through the crack of the door ? "

The little black cat opened his eyes and stared too ; then he got up from his place by the fireside and walked across to the door. He seemed to listen a moment and then he looked at Mother Jennifer and said as plainly as a cat could say with his eyes, "Open the door, Mother Jennifer!" and Mother Jennifer did as she was bid. She could see nothing at first except darkness, and she could hear nothing but the

wind whistling and moaning over the moor. Then suddenly, from somewhere down by her feet, came a long shrill squeal, " Oe-ee-oo-ee-oo-ee-ee-ee ! " Mother Jennifer jumped and somebody gave a little cackling laugh. And the little black cat pounced into the dark as if he was catching a rat, and whisked back again with a little kicking brown bundle and laid it at Mother Jennifer's feet. And as Mother Jennifer stooped to look the brown bundle uncurled and shook itself and scrambled to its feet. It was a tiny man in brown—the colour of withered bracken—with a red cap and a brown wrinkled face that looked as if he might be as " old as the hills," as the saying goes.

" Cats never can take a joke," said the little man in a shrill, squeaky voice. The little black cat walked away in a dignified manner and sat down with his back turned and his tail folded over his toes.

" All I wanted," said the little man, " was just to ask for a little meal for my little bag, and he treats me like a rat ! "

" People that squeal and squeak like rats should be treated like rats," said Mother Jennifer severely. " Last time I saw one of you hill-folk " (a hill-man is a fairy-man, as we should say) " *he* was in mischief too, tangling up my wool as fast as I spun it, and the time before he was tweaking the hens' tails, and they've never laid an egg since, poor creatures. How do I know what mischief you may be up to to-night ? "

"Nothing at all—nothing at all, Mother Jennifer," said the little man. "I only want to borrow a little meal to make a little cake for my mother's birthday. A thousand years old she is to-night, as you count time, and she fancies an oaten cake. You shall have the meal back in no time at all, I promise you."

Mother Jennifer stood considering. There was very little meal in the meal-chest, as you know, and every little counts when you have yourself and your cat and a goat and two hens to feed, as she certainly would if the snow came down that night. But it did seem as if a person who had had nine hundred and ninety-nine birthdays, and who was going to have another, ought to have what she wanted. So Mother Jennifer opened the lid of the meal-chest and said to the little brown man, "Help yourself and welcome." He scrambled in and began to fill his bag in a great hurry. It was surprising how long he took and how much his bag seemed to hold. Now and again he looked at Mother Jennifer with his sharp brown eyes ; but she said nothing to stop him, and at last he had stuffed in every grain there was room for. And then he gave a sudden jump, just like a brown cricket, and was gone, bag and all, out of the door, which

152

was still a crack open, and into the dark. And the little black cat got up and rubbed himself against Mother Jennifer, as much as to say, " Never mind, *we* know what manners are, even if he doesn't ! "  Then he curled himself up by the fire, and presently Mother Jennifer went to bed too, and she and all her family slept snug and warm that night.

But outside it snowed and snowed. The heather and the furze and the grass were covered deep ; so was the long, straight road, and there were drifts in all the hollows. When Mother Jennifer woke in the morning the little house was almost dark, and she could scarcely open the door for the weight of snow against it. And still the air seemed full of snow, falling, falling, like cold grey feathers from the cold grey sky.

Mother Jennifer milked the nanny-goat and gave her a piece of oatcake, and she gave some to the hens too. Then she set some porridge on to boil, and by and by she and the little black cat had breakfast. There was a little porridge for dinner too, and some for supper as well. But the meal chest was nearly empty, and what could she do when all the meal was gone ! She sat by the fire a long time that evening, wondering unhappily, whether poor Speckle and Brownie, who had never laid an egg since the hill-man tweaked their tails, would have to be made into chicken broth before the snow melted and the roads were clear again. At last she fell asleep and woke once in the night to hear a little scratching sound as if a rat was burrowing under the hearthstone. She could just see the little black cat sitting beside the red embers, with his ears pricked, watching ; so she said " Good Pussy," and went to sleep again.

When she woke in the morning and went to the meal chest to see if she could scrape a little meal together, the first thing she saw was the hill-man's little bag lying on the lid of the chest, stuffed as fat and tight as when he took it away. " The good little creature ! " said Mother Jennifer, " it will give the hens a meal, poor things." She opened the bag and began to pour out a little stream of oatmeal for the hens to peck at. It trickled steadily out of the little brown bag—more and more came out till there was quite a little heap ; and the bag seemed as full as ever.

"They give good measure," said Mother Jennifer to the little black cat and the nanny goat and the hens, who were all watching her. And still the meal poured out and the bag felt fat and firm.

"There's enough to make porridge for to-day," she said presently. So she put the little brown bag away in the meal chest—it still seemed as full as ever—and she cooked a large potful of porridge and they all had some for breakfast and dinner and supper. (You might have been tired of porridge, but Mother Jennifer and the little black cat and the goat and the hens didn't mind ; besides, it was very good porridge—very good

indeed.) And would you believe it, next day Speckle laid an egg ! The little brown bag still poured out oatmeal to feed them all ; and the next day but one Brownie laid an egg ! The fairy porridge must have quite cured them of their fright you see, and there was no more need to think of making them into chicken broth.

So it went on all through the long dark days and nights when the snow lay deep on the moor till one day the wind changed and the sun shone and the drifts melted, and by and by the miller's man was able to come ploughing through the snow with Mother Jennifer's bag of meal.

And what became of the hill-man's bag, do you ask ? It vanished away somehow, when the meal chest was full again. Some folk thought that the nanny-goat had eaten it—goats will eat *anything* you know. But most people said the hill-man had taken it away again, and I think they were right. Most likely the little black cat knew, but cats don't talk, and he never told anyone what really happened.

COMMENTS ON THE STORY

The story of " The Hill-man's Little Bag " is founded on a tale of the coast of Buchan, where, tradition says, there once lived a farmer's wife who lent a handful of meal to " a little woman." Later, the meal was returned with the saying, " Put it in the meal chest and never want again." And the meal lasted through three weeks of heavy snow which followed her visit, so that the household was fed while the roads were closed.

The original is very brief, and I must explain that I have no authority for Mother Jennifer's family. Like Topsy of " Uncle Tom's Cabin," they " growed." Also, since I knew that I could not do justice to the speech of Buchan, I transferred the dame to a Northumbrian moor and framed her conversation according to the ordinary undistinguished manner of fairy tales.

It is interesting to note that in this—as in all other folk tales of the type—the " Good Folk " have no difficulty in restoring—fourfold or a hundredfold, it may be—the very thing that want compels them to borrow. The idea seems to be that they can multiply but not originate. But there is more than that " to it."

For it is not mere giving that sets the charm working ; it is generous, free-handed giving, " asking for nothing again." " Kindly welcome " is still the pleasant country phrase that responds to thanks for a gift received ; and a gift in such a spirit is the only one that is acceptable to the " Good Folk." Gifts, bestowed grudgingly, or in hopes of reward, seem to turn their goodwill to venom and spite.

Such tales as these, it is said, belong to the childhood of the race, and our sophisticated minds sometimes despise them as childish and trivial. Yet I think there is often in their childishness something of that wise simplicity and understanding which belong to those " little children " concerning whom we are told that " of such is the kingdom of heaven."

THE TALE OF MR T TOAD AND MR LITTLEFROG

XII

THERE was once a pleasant little pool that lay in the corner of a large green field. Tall reeds and rushes grew round it in a ring, and beyond them were thorn bushes and brambles. So the little pool was hidden away from everyone but the birds who flew over it and the dragon flies that sometimes floated above it.

Down among the reeds and rushes on the edge of the pool lived Mr. T. Toad and his friend Mr. Littlefrog. There were little fishes in the pool and snails and beetles and water spiders and other creepy-crawly things, but Mr. T.

Toad was far larger than any of them—even Mr. Littlefrog looked a very small fellow beside him—and there was no doubt he thought himself far more important, and so did everyone else. Nobody ever thought of calling him just " Mr. Toad " ; they always called him " Mr. T. Toad." But no one knew what the T. stood for. It might have been Thomas or it might have been Timothy, or even Theophilus ; nobody, not even Mr. Littlefrog, quite liked to ask him. But the fishes and the beetles and the water snails and spiders all believed it really stood for " Tremendous." He was so very proud and grand.

He would sit for hours by the edge of the pool looking at himself in the clear shining water and puffing himself out to look as large as possible. Mr. Littlefrog would sit by his side admiring him too, while the fishes popped their heads out of the water to watch, and said to each other, " How wonderful to have such a great gentleman living amongst us. He must be quite the largest creature in the whole world." They really believed it. So did Mr. T. Toad and Mr. Littlefrog, and nobody ever came near them to tell them they were wrong. The ground was so marshy and the reeds and rushes so tall and thick that no animals came to drink at the little pool.

So there they all lived together—Mr. T. Toad, Mr. Littlefrog, the beetles, the snails, the water spiders and the fishes—and they would have been as happy as the day was long if it had not been for Mr. T. Toad's temper. No one could call him a good-tempered toad. You see, he was quite sure that the pool belonged to him, and was meant for him to use as a looking-glass. And if a fish ruffled it, or a water spider ran across it while he was sitting there, or if Mr. Littlefrog jumped in " plop " and made rings all over it, Mr. T. Toad was very angry indeed. Then he would sit scolding while everyone shivered and shook to listen to him ; and they were all very thankful when he stopped talking and hopped slowly and grumpily away among the bulrush roots and went to sleep.

The times that everyone looked forward to and enjoyed were the days on which Mr. T. Toad changed his coat. He did not change it very often, because you see his coat was not like yours or mine would be. It grew upon his back and fitted him very comfortably, and his new coat grew underneath the old one. When he was ready to change, " Pop " went the old coat and it split, and Mr. T. Toad wriggled out of it and rolled it up into a neat little ball and *swallowed* it.

But he did not wish the fishes or the beetles or the water spider or snails—or even his friend Mr. Littlefrog—to see him half in and half out of his coat. So when the time came he always hopped away among the reeds and rushes and spent the day where no one could watch him.

Those were beautiful days. The fishes swam round and round the pool ; the water spiders raced across and across ; Mr. Littlefrog dived in and out ; the snails and beetles crawled up and down the stems of the water plants. Everyone played and was happy till Mr. T. Toad came hopping heavily out of the bulrushes in his fine new coat and sat down to admire himself in the clear water.

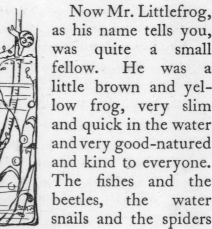

Now Mr. Littlefrog, as his name tells you, was quite a small fellow. He was a little brown and yellow frog, very slim and quick in the water and very good-natured and kind to everyone. The fishes and the beetles, the water snails and the spiders all liked him. He had plenty of friends to talk to and play with. Sometimes he felt sorry for Mr. T. Toad. " Poor fellow ! " he said to himself. " It must be very lonely to be so much greater than everyone else that you have nobody grand enough to talk to."

Well, one day—it was early in the summer and everyone was feeling very happy and gay—Mr. T. Toad's temper seemed worse than usual. I think it may have been because his coat was growing tight and uncomfortable ; it was almost time for him to change it. And as Mr. Littlefrog looked at poor sulky Mr. T. Toad he said to himself, " A little friendly conversation would do him a world of good. After all, there may be someone to keep him company. I will see what I can do." And he turned his back on the pleasant little pool and all his gay companions and hopped bravely away through the bulrushes to the edge of the marsh. It was just like travelling through a tall forest would be to you or me, and he had never been so far before. Presently he came to thorn bushes and brambles, and it was not easy to find his way through them ; but he managed it at last and found himself in a field of grass and tall yellow buttercups. Through the field there ran a little stream which came from the pool where Mr. Littlefrog lived. And munching the long grass by the side of the stream was a creature so much larger than Mr. T. Toad that Mr. Littlefrog could hardly believe his eyes. It had a brown and white coat and large brown eyes ; it had two horns on its head and a long tail. And as Mr. Littlefrog stared at it, the creature lifted its head and said, "Moo-oo-oo-oo-oo," and from the other end of the field another creature answered, " Moo-oo-oo-oo-oo ! "

It was only a cow, of course, talking to another cow, but it seemed terribly large and noisy to

Mr. Littlefrog, and he turned round and hopped back to the marsh as quickly as his legs could carry him, with his heart beating very fast and his long legs shaking with fright. He scrambled through the bushes and scuffled through the reeds till he reached

the edge of the pool ; and there sat Mr. T. Toad admiring himself in the clear water while the fishes nudged each other and whispered, " Keep quiet, he is very cross to-day."

" Oh, Mr. T. Toad ! Mr. T. Toad," said Mr. Littlefrog, all out of breath and in a great hurry, " I have some wonderful news for you."

And Mr. T. Toad, without even turning his head, said, " Pray do not be so noisy. You disturb me."

" But Mr. T. Toad," said Mr. Littlefrog, " you need not be lonely any longer, for you are not the largest creature in the world. There are others far larger to keep you company." And all the fishes poked out their heads to listen, and whispered to each other, " Fancy that ! "

But Mr. T. Toad, still without turning his head, said, " Pooh ! " which was very rude of him. One should not say " Pooh " to kind people who are trying to tell one things.

" But it is quite true, Mr. T. Toad," said Mr. Littlefrog. " I have seen the creature."

" Pooh ! " said Mr. T. Toad again. " Is it as large as this ? " And he puffed out his sides till he looked like a fat little puppy-dog.

" *Much* larger," said Mr. Littlefrog.

" Rubbish ! " said Mr. T. Toad, and he

 puffed out his sides till he looked like a football.

"Much, *much* larger, dear Mr. T. Toad," said Mr. Littlefrog earnestly.

"*Stuff*!" said Mr. T. Toad very loudly. And he gave a great puff, and *pop*! his coat split all down the middle of his back. And a small fish, whose manners were not very good, laughed till it swallowed some water and choked, and then all the other fishes laughed too. They really could not help it.

But Mr. T. Toad was very angry and very much upset, and he turned round and hopped away among the bulrush roots as fast as he could go, with his torn coat flapping round him like a mackintosh.

And he never came back! Perhaps he hopped away and found the cow and settled down in the field by the side of the stream ; perhaps he found another pond where nobody could laugh at him, and lived there all alone. Perhaps he tried so hard to blow himself up as big as a cow that he blew himself up altogether and flew into little bits. Nobody knows.

Mr. Littlefrog and the fishes and the beetles and the water spiders and the snails often used to wonder what had become of him, but they could never really be sorry he had gone. He had been so cross and they were so comfortable without him. So they talked and played their games and chased each other round and round, and ruffled the water just as much as they pleased. And they all lived as happy as the day was long in that pleasant little pool down among the reeds and bulrushes, where nobody ever came to trouble them or scold them.

COMMENTS ON THE STORY

Those who know Æsop's Fables—and what story-teller does not—will, of course, recognise " The Tale of Mr. T. Toad and Mr. Littlefrog " as a modified version of the fable of the frog who tried to swell himself to the size of an ox and who burst in the trying.

The fable, being designed to convey a moral to the world in general, is short and sharply pointed. But since " The Tale of Mr. T. Toad and Mr. Littlefrog " is intended for children, I have aimed mainly at making the story live as clear and friendly pictures, leaving the moral to take care of itself, as it may usually be trusted to do, I think, if the story-teller is really entering into the interest of the story.

Now it must always be borne in mind that conveying pictures to one's listeners is not merely a matter of memorising words and details. It goes deeper than this. Before we can *show* pictures we must ourselves *see* them. Most of us can do this more easily and more clearly than we realise. We have the power of visualising but we do not exercise it ; we are content to let our mental pictures remain vague, hazy, and half seen.

But if we take the trouble to pause over our story, to consider it, to look and look again at the impressions we have gained, we shall see that the pictures are there, " in our mind's eye," and, detail by detail, they will sharpen and grow clear. The little pool among the bulrushes becomes real to us, we see the clear brown water, the tall green bulrush leaves. We pick out here a head of feathery grass, there a little edge of smooth, oozy mud. We find that Mr. T. Toad has established himself at one particular spot. We do not place him there. He *is* there : and we are quite sure where Mr. Littlefrog is sitting and where the water is dotted with the heads of admiring and investigating fishes.

And as we follow the course of the story we shall find—*if we look*—that scene by scene it is there to watch. So seeing, we tell—not conscientiously by rote, not with our minds didactically set upon the doom of such as are puffed with pride and the warning that we must convey to our listeners, but as a good story-teller should, delighting in our story and bent on sharing the pleasant pictures which we see, with those who listen.

I think we should rehearse the dialogue between Mr. T. Toad and Mr. Littlefrog—rehearse it aloud, that is—before telling. This will help to memorise it (dialogue should always go clearly and without a hitch), and it will also bring out the necessary degrees of haughty contempt, incredulity, surprise and exasperation with which Mr. T. Toad receives the earnest and well-meant expostulations of his ingenuous friend Mr. Littlefrog.

The " pop " of the final catastrophe should also be studied. It must be decisive, impressive and explosive !

In conclusion, I should add that the story was originally intended, like the original, to have a frog as its central figure, " Mr. Jonathan Bull-

frog " by name. But I discovered, at the last
moment, that frogs only shed a transparent
membrane ; they do not change their skins. So
in the interests of truth it was necessary to replace
" Mr. Jonathan Bullfrog " by " Mr. T. Toad."

The TALE of DOBBIN and the SILVER SHOES

XIII

IT was a very fine day early in June. The sun was shining, the sky was blue, the hedges were full of dog roses, and the wind blew soft. But Mistress Mary Jane was walking up and down a field of buttercups and grass and clover, looking at the ground and crying as she walked. Big round tears—about two-to-a-teaspoonful size—were running down her cheeks, and she was saying, "I can't see one—not one—not even a little one." She was talking to herself; there was no one else to talk to, except an old white horse standing by the hedge and a stout brown rabbit that was hopping up and down the field, taking no more notice of Mistress Mary Jane than Mistress Mary Jane was taking of him.

Mistress Mary Jane lived in the white cottage just across the road. It had a garden full of flowers in front and a yard full of chickens behind. There was another field with a black and white cow ; there was a sty with a nice little pig, and a tabby cat was washing itself on the cottage doorstep. Mistress Mary Jane was rosy-cheeked and fat and comfortable. You would have thought she had everything in the world to make her happy that fine sunshiny day ; and yet here she was crying, and the old white horse looked just as unhappy as she did.

And now I will tell you what the trouble was. The old white horse had gone lame. He had been all right only the evening before, but when Mistress Mary Jane came into his field on the day this story happened, he could hardly move. His mane and his tail were full of tangles, and he looked as if someone had galloped him far and fast. And next day Mistress Mary Jane was to go to a wedding ten miles away. It was her brother John's wedding, and she had a new bonnet with cherry-coloured ribbons and a new sprigged muslin gown. There was a pot of honey, three pounds of fresh butter, and some new-laid eggs, all ready to be packed in a basket. And at eight o'clock the next morning Mistress Mary Jane had meant to climb on to Dobbin's broad back and go jogging away, with her basket on her arm, down the green lanes to the wedding.

And now Dobbin was lame, and Mistress Mary Jane was quite sure it was the Fairies who had been galloping him round the field all night. (There was a great fairy ring in the middle of the field so she knew the Good Folk came there.) So she was hunting up and down the field for a four-leaf clover, because as everyone knows, if you can find a four-leaf clover the Fairies cannot play tricks with you. If only she could find one she meant to go to the fairy ring that night to give the Fairies what she called " a proper good talking to," and to tell them that they must cure Dobbin of his lameness before the next morning.

But for all her searching she could not find a four-leaf clover. It seemed there was not one in the whole green field. Mistress Mary Jane's back ached, her temper ached; she was hot and tired and cross and disappointed, and that was why she was crying. And just at the minute this story begins, a very big tear rolled down her cheek and fell splash !—right in the middle of a clover leaf. And Mistress Mary Jane looked down and said : " I do believe that's one ! "

But when she stooped and picked it, it was not a four-leaf, but a *five*-leaf clover.

As she stood looking at it, a very odd thing happened. The stout brown rabbit that was hopping up and down the field nibbling at the grass and clover suddenly turned round and came hopping across the field to Mistress Mary Jane. And when he reached her, he sat and looked at her, and there was a four-leaf clover hanging out of his mouth. And then a still more odd thing happened. The stout brown rabbit began to talk !

" At your service, Mum," he said. " Please to take the clover."

Mistress Mary Jane stooped down and took it. " Wherever did you find it ? I couldn't see one," was the only thing she could find to say. She was so very surprised, and I really don't wonder—do you ?

"I've been eating them all the morning," said the stout brown rabbit. "I'm caretaker of this field, Mum, and I had my orders to eat every four-leaf clover before you could find it. But the Good Folk" (he meant the Fairies, you know) "forgot that it is Leap Year. And if you find a five-leaf clover in Leap Year you can come and go as you like for twenty-four hours by day *or* by night. Elves, Pixies, Fairies, Good Folk, can't stop you. So if I was you, Mum, I should come here after sunset this evening and talk to the Little Folk. Bring both the clovers with you, and you'll get what you want."

"Thank you. So I will," said Mistress Mary Jane. She had stopped being surprised, and it seemed quite natural to be talking to a rabbit; perhaps it was because of the five-leaf clover. She went over to the old white horse and patted him comfortably. Then she went back to her cottage and put the clover leaves in water, and had her dinner. And afterwards she finished trimming her bonnet with cherry-coloured ribbons and packed the butter and honey and eggs. She was quite sure everything was going to be all right now that she had her clover leaves.

The sun does not set till past nine in June-time, as you will see if you look in the calendar. So about half-past nine Mistress Mary Jane went across the road to the field with both her clovers safe in her hand.   It was still quite light, and she could see old Dobbin standing with his ears pricked watching the fairy ring.   Mistress Mary Jane could see nobody, but the stout brown rabbit was waiting for her, and he said : " Please to come inside, Mum," and he hopped inside the ring, and Mistress Mary Jane stepped after him.   She could still see nobody ; but the grass blades all round the ring were shaking and quivering, although there was not a breath of wind.   The stout brown rabbit seemed to be listening to something she could not hear.   She could see his ears twitching, and presently he said : " They want to know, Mum, will you have the old horse nimble-and-quick or steady-and-strong ? "

" Steady-and-strong," said Mistress Mary Jane in a great hurry, thinking of the butter and eggs and her own fat, comfortable self.

And as she spoke, it was like throwing a stone into a still pool.   You know how the ripples spread and spread.   The grass blades quivered and shook, and all round the ring she could hear clear little voices saying, " Steady-and-strong, steady-and-strong,   steady-and-strong,   steady-

and-strong," fainter and fainter and fainter, farther and farther away, till all was quiet again.

" *That's* all right, Mum," said the stout brown rabbit, " and now, if I was you, I should just go home to bed." And so she did, and she slept soundly till the birds woke up and began to talk to each other at daybreak.

" Bless me," said Mistress Mary Jane as she woke, " it's brother John's wedding day." And then she remembered about Dobbin and the Fairies, and she jumped out of bed and looked out. The sun was not up, but the sky was golden in the east and pale clear blue overhead. She could see Dobbin in his field. He seemed to be standing in the fairy ring. Mistress Mary Jane bustled about and into her lilac print dress. (It was too early to dress for the wedding, of course.) She put on a pair of clogs. " The meadow will be sopped with dew," she said. And she picked up her clover leaves and hurried down the garden path and across the road. As she reached the gate of the field, the stout brown rabbit popped out of the hedge to meet her.

" Please to come this way, Mum," he said, and he hopped across the field in front of her to the fairy ring. And there stood Dobbin most splendid to behold. His mane and his tail were like white silk, so glossy and bright ; his coat was like the finest white satin, and he was shod with four brand-new, beautiful, silver-shining shoes.

"There he is, Mum," said the stout brown rabbit, proudly, "steady-and-strong and just

fit for a wedding." And, "Yes, *indeed*," said Mistress Mary Jane. And she went and stood by Dobbin in the fairy ring and picked up her lilac print skirts and dropped a very deep curtsey, and said : "Thank you kindly, all Good Folk, with all my heart."

"You're very welcome, Mum," said the stout brown rabbit, and the grass blades round the ring quivered and shook, and Mistress Mary Jane could hear clear little voices saying : "Welcome, welcome, welcome, welcome," from farther and farther away, just like spreading ripples on a pond. And then a little wind came rustling across the meadow, and a long ray of sunlight came with it. The sun was up and all the dew-drops sparkled and shone and danced. The sun was up, and Mistress Mary Jane could see her shadow and Dobbin's lying long and dark on the bright green grass.

The stout brown rabbit was nibbling grass and clover with his little shadow beside him. He did not seem to have any more to say, so Mistress Mary Jane went back to the gate with Dobbin following her. His lameness had quite  gone and he seemed as steady and strong as anyone could wish. She patted his shining coat and went back to her kitchen. And when she had milked the cow and fed the chickens and the little black pig, and given the cat a saucer of milk and eaten her own breakfast, Mistress Mary

Jane dressed herself in the sprigged muslin and the bonnet with cherry-coloured ribbons, and climbed on to Dobbin's back with her basket of eggs and honey and butter. And away they went jogging through the green lanes to the wedding. And when she got there everyone said that Dobbin, with his silver-shining shoes, was the handsomest horse that ever they had seen.

I don't know what the shoes were made of, but they never wore out. For many and many a day Mistress Mary Jane and Dobbin jogged along together, " Steady-and-strong, steady-and-strong, steady-and-strong," as the stout brown rabbit had said. As for the rabbit, Mistress Mary Jane often saw him hopping about the field, but he never spoke to her again. The clover-leaf magic only lasted for twenty-four hours, you see. She pressed the leaves in Doctor Johnson's Dictionary, and sometimes when her neighbours came in for a cup of tea she let them have a peep and told them the story of the four-leaf clover and the five-leaf clover, and Dobbin's silver-shining shoes.

COMMENTS ON THE STORY

I think that a good deal of the telling of such a story as this depends upon how far we have seen it as a series of pictures.   To begin with we need a kind of map in our heads, or on paper—but a map there must be.   It is always well in considering any story to see things in their relative positions ; then we can move freely, accompanying our characters as a story-teller should.   Here, it will be noticed that the cottage, with its flower garden and hedge, faced Dobbin's field, with a road between.   Obviously also the cottage faced east, for Mistress Mary Jane could see the light of the rising sun as she looked towards the field.   Why trouble about this ?   Because once we have things reasonably clear in our own minds, a hundred little details of form and colour will light up our picture for us.

And now let us look.   First, there is a contrast— the garden and cottage backing in the noon sunlight, a comfortable noise of hens clucking and crooning, a peaceful pig and a contented cow, green leaves on trees and hedgerows ; and poor, lame, dishevelled Dobbin, and a disturbed Mistress Mary Jane, hot and tired and cross, seeking a four-leaf clover and weeping as she goes.

Then the stout brown rabbit intervenes. He is astonishing, but as befits a caretaker, very matter-of-fact in his speech and behaviour, and all the more astonishing for that.   He has rather a long speech to make (longer than I like ; speeches in stories should not be long. But I could not get it " said " in any other way). It should be given in the tone one would use in giving any ordinary explanation or direction. When he has finished, Mistress Mary Jane has accepted the situation. Everyone feels more comfortable, and the afternoon goes by in pleasant, sleepy contentment.

Evening comes, and now look : the sky behind the white cottage is all clear gold, a star or two is shining faint in the pale blue above. The sharp shadows that sunlight gives are gone. After sunset there is dusk, not defined shadows. In the still light we see Dobbin standing patiently; the stout brown rabbit is waiting, and Mistress Mary Jane steps into the fairy ring. Watch and see the grass blades quiver ; listen and hear tiny elfin echoes round the ring. And then with Mistress Mary Jane we go back to the familiar homeliness of the white cottage " and so to bed."

Then dawn, and now look : light in the east, faint blue overhead. It is clear shadowless light ; evening light seems to gather up and intensify colour, but dawn light stills and quiets. Dew lies on the grass and birds are calling, but the world is only half awake ; even Mistress Mary Jane in her lilac print and clogs is under the spell of the hour that " is neither dark nor day." Look at Dobbin, white and sleek and silver-shod in the still dawn light. See Mistress Mary Jane in her lilac gown stoop to her magnificent curtsey with the stout brown rabbit beside her. And hear the clear little echoes ringing fainter across the field, till they are swept away by the wind that runs before the sunrise.

Then all flashes into life—the green grass hung with dewdrops, the tall trees, the hedgerows. The sky takes a fuller blue, the shadows are long and sharp and clear. The work-a-day business of life, with its cheerful homeliness, begins, and presently we watch Mistress Mary Jane and Dobbin go jogging through green lanes to the wedding. And let us not forget to notice how beautiful they both are looking, and how unlike the doleful pair that first we met.

The conclusion can be used or not. I always like to end up a story tidily and comfortably, but if this one seems too long-winded it can very well stop at the wedding.

The appellations " Mistress Mary Jane " and " the stout brown rabbit " seem to recur rather often, I admit. But experience has shown me that a little pomposity in names and epithets adds to the effect of a story. The rabbit is not *any* rabbit ; he is a Stout Brown Rabbit and a Caretaker. And Mistress Mary Jane is as full-blown as her name. Let us give each their due.

Finally, if there are any story-tellers who like— as I do myself—to know there is some precedent for a story, let them note that in Thyholm, Denmark, a peasant lamented that his horse whereon he rode to market was but a sorry jade. And the said horse was mysteriously provided by the elf folk with such marvellous shoes that no other horse in all the countryside could go so far and fast.